CONTENTS

The *Mill* on the *Floss*

George Eliot

Retold by Maud Jackson
Activities by Justin Rainey

Editors: Elvira Poggi Repetto, Frances Evans
Design: Nadia Maestri
Illustrations: Didi Coppola

© 2002   Black Cat Publishing,
         an imprint of Cideb Editrice, Genoa, Canterbury

We would be happy to receive your comments and suggestions, and give you
any other information concerning our material. Our e-mail and web-site addresses
are: info@blackcat-cideb.com
http://www.blackcat-cideb.com

ISBN 88-7754-798-7 Book + CD
ISBN 88-7754-873-8 Book

Printed in Italy by Litoprint, Genoa

PART 5   THE FINAL RESCUE

 These signs mark the beginning and end of the recorded parts of the text.

George Eliot and
The Mill on the Floss

George Eliot (1849)
by Francois D'Albert-Durade.
National Portrait Gallery, London.

Mary Ann Evans (later known as George Eliot) was born in 1819 at South Farm in Warwickshire. Her father was a farm manager, and her mother ran a dairy. [1] Although no one else in her family was well-educated, Mary Ann developed a scholarly turn of mind. She read widely in literature and theology and, by the time she was twenty, could read in several languages. As a girl, Mary Ann was very religious, but in the 1840s she came to doubt and finally to renounce her Christian faith. She translated two important books of Biblical criticism from German to English. After her father's death she moved to London, where she worked as a writer and editor. There she met and fell in love with George Henry Lewes. Lewes was already married and could not obtain a divorce. In 1854, he and Mary Ann began living together as husband and wife. This was a great scandal in London society and, throughout her life with Lewes (from 1854 to 1878, when he died), Mary Ann was considered a fallen woman.

In 1857, she started writing fiction, using the pseudonym 'George Eliot'. Her stories met with great success, and the reading public were very curious about who George Eliot really was. Her true identity was kept secret for the first two years, but then it became generally known that England's new great novelist was in fact Mary Ann Evans, the scandalous woman who lived with a married man.

---

1. **dairy** : part of farm where cheese and butter are made.

The Mill on the Floss is in some ways an autobiographical novel. Mary Ann, like Maggie, had a brother whom she loved very much. Mary Ann's brother Isaac, like Tom, was severe and judgmental. Isaac never forgave Mary Ann for living with Lewes. *The Mill on the Floss* is the story of an honest, passionate, intelligent woman with strong desires. In trying to satisfy her desires, she gains the disapproval of her family and the society in which she lives, and yet she is in many ways a better person than those who condemn her. It is also a story about nature and nurture, [1] about genetic inheritance and education, published a year after the appearance of Darwin's *On the Origin of Species.*

---

1. **nurture** : protection, care.

A C T I V I T I E S

1 What is the significance of the following dates in Mary Ann Evans' life? Complete the table.

Date	Event
1819	
1840s	
1854	
1857	
1878	

2 Conventions

Different historical periods have different social conventions. What is usual or unsurprising today was very different in mid-Victorian England. Supply the missing information on the basis of the text.

Mid-Victorian England	Surprising:	England today	Surprising:
	Unsurprising:		Unsurprising:

3 *The Mill on the Floss* is in some ways autobiographical. What are the similarities between Mary Ann Evans and Maggie, and Isaac Evans and Tom? Bear these in mind when you read the story.

CHILDHOOD

CHAPTER ◆ 1

Dorlcote Mill

The town of St Ogg's on the River Floss is a busy, lively, flourishing place. Ships pass up and down the river, bringing coal and timber [1] and taking away the delicious cheeses and fine woollen cloth produced in the town. It is one of those old, old towns that seem part of nature. Beyond its red roofs and great warehouses, [2] the fields stretch [3] green and fruitful to the horizon, and the River Floss hurries to meet the sea. People have lived here since Roman times, and the town bears the traces of its long history. The old Hall was built by the Normans, and the ruined chapel is older still. This was the original chapel dedicated to St Ogg, the patron saint of the town.

According to the legend, Ogg was a boatman who earned a modest living taking passengers across the River Floss. One stormy evening he saw a poor ragged [4] woman with a child in her arms standing on the river bank, weeping. Ogg asked her why she wept, and she said that none of the boatmen would take her across the river, because the weather was bad and she had no money. Ogg said to the woman, 'I will take you across the river, if that is your heart's desire.' And he took her across. When the woman stepped out of the boat on the other

---

1. **timber** : wood.
2. **warehouses** : buildings where goods are stored.
3. **stretch** : extend.
4. **ragged** [rægɪd] : wearing old and torn clothes.

shore, her ragged clothes turned into flowing white robes, [1] and her tired face became bright and beautiful, and light shone from her like the light of the moon. And she said, 'Ogg, you are blessed, because you did not question the heart's desire. From now on, your boat will never be in danger from the storm, and if you set out to rescue drowning people, you will save their lives.' And, when the floods [2] came, many were saved by Ogg and his blessed boat. When Ogg died, the boat floated down the river to the sea and was never seen again. But years later, in times of flood, people claimed [3] to have seen Ogg in his boat and with him the Virgin Mary, shining as bright as the moon.

Standing today on the green bank of the River Floss, it is hard to imagine those distant times of floods and miracles. The sound of the river is low and placid as I walk along but, as I get closer to Dorlcote Mill, I hear the rush [4] of the water booming. [5] It makes me feel deaf and dreamy. I remember that stone bridge, those dripping willow trees, and the ducks diving head first into the water. I can see the mill wheel, sending out its diamond jets of water. That little girl is watching it too. It is time she went home. The sky is getting dark and the air is cold, but inside the house the red light of the fire is waiting for her, and her parents – Mr and Mrs Tulliver – are sitting by the fire, talking to each other...

'What I want,' said Mr Tulliver, 'is to give Tom a good education. I want to put him in a good school, so that he can learn to read and write and speak well. The Academy, where he is now, is all right for farmers' sons, but I want Tom to be a gentleman. Then he will be able to understand these terrible lawyers who give me so much trouble.

---

1. **robes** : elegant clothing.
2. **floods** : inundations of water.
3. **claimed** : (here) said.
4. **rush** : quick movement.
5. **booming** : loud, deep sound.

He will be able to help me in my lawsuits.'[1]

Mr Tulliver was speaking to his wife, a pretty blonde woman. 'Well, Mr Tulliver,' she replied, 'I suppose you are right. But shall I invite the aunts and uncles over, so that you can ask them about it?'

'Bessy!' said Mr Tulliver angrily. 'You can invite your sisters and their husbands if you wish, but I don't need their advice about what to do with my own son!'

'Why must you get so angry?' asked Mrs Tulliver. 'You never did like my family. My sister Mrs Glegg blames me, but it's not my fault. I've always been proud of my family, and I'm glad that my children have such respectable uncles and aunts. If you must send Tom away to school, don't send him too far.'

'Don't worry, Bessy. I've heard of a good school that's not too far away. But sometimes I think Tom hasn't got the kind of brain to be an educated man. He seems a bit slow. He takes after[2] your family, Bessy.'

'He certainly does,' said Mrs Tulliver, not noticing the insult. 'He has our blond hair and blue eyes.'

'It's unfortunate, though,' said Mr Tulliver, 'that the boy should take after his mother instead of the girl. The girl takes after my family. She's twice as clever as Tom. Too clever for a woman. It's no problem while she's little, but when she grows up she'll have trouble finding a husband.'

'It *is* a problem while she's little, Mr Tulliver, because it makes her naughty. She is always getting her clothes dirty, and I never know where she is.' Mrs Tulliver went to the window. 'Where is she now, by the way? It's almost tea time. Ah! There she is. Walking by the water as usual. She'll fall in one day.'

Mrs Tulliver knocked on the window and beckoned[3] to her daughter. 'You say she's clever, but I think she's almost an idiot

---

1. **lawsuits** : procedures of bringing a dispute before a lawcourt.
2. **takes after** : resembles, has inherited characteristics from.
3. **beckoned** : gestured with her hand to come nearer.

sometimes. If I send her upstairs to get something, she forgets what she has gone for. She just sits down in the sunshine by the window and starts singing to herself like an idiot, while I'm waiting for her downstairs. No one in my family ever did that sort of thing, thank God! And her skin is so brown that she looks like a gypsy. It's a pity I only have one daughter, and she is so strange.'

'Nonsense!' said Mr Tulliver. 'She's a good-looking girl, and she reads better than anyone else's children.'

'But her hair won't curl, and she won't stand still while I try to make it look nice.'

'Cut it off, then,' said Mr Tulliver. 'Cut it short!'

'Don't be ridiculous, Mr Tulliver! She's nine years old – too old to have short hair. Her cousin Lucy has such lovely curls, and her hair is always tidy. It's not fair that my sister Mrs Deane should have such a pretty daughter. Lucy looks more like me than my own daughter does.'

At that moment, Mrs Tulliver's daughter came into the room. 'Oh, Maggie!' said Mrs Tulliver. 'I told you to keep away from the water. You'll fall in and drown one day.'

Maggie took off her hat, revealing the messy [1] hair that so distressed [2] her mother, then she took her book and sat down on the floor by her father's feet to read it. With her shining black eyes and thick dark hair, she looked like a wild pony.

'What are you reading, Maggie?' asked Mr Tulliver.

'It's called *The History of the Devil* by Mr Daniel Defoe. It's a very interesting book, Father. Look at this picture. It's a terrible picture, isn't it? But I can't help looking at it. That old woman in the water is a witch. They put her in the water to find out whether she is a witch or not. If she drowns, they will know she was not a witch. But what good will that do her when she's dead? And this terrible man watching and laughing is really the devil!'

---

1. **messy** : untidy.
2. **distressed** : caused suffering.

'Good Lord!' cried Mrs Tulliver. 'That's not the kind of book a little girl should be reading! Maggie, go and brush your hair. Then come down and do your sewing, ¹ as a little lady should.'

'But, Mother, I don't want to do my sewing!' said Maggie. 'It's stupid work!' And, with her book under her arm, she walked out of the room. Mr Tulliver laughed with delight.

'What are you laughing at?' asked Mrs Tulliver. 'You encourage her to be naughty. Then her aunts blame me for it.'

---

1. **sewing** : the making or repairing of clothes or other items.

A C T I V I T I E S

Unless otherwise stated, you should do the exercises with a partner. Then write your answers in your notebook.

1 Why is the town called St Ogg's?

2 How is Maggie different from her brother Tom and her cousin Lucy?

3 What plans does Mr Tulliver have for his son, Tom?

4 Mr Tulliver says about Tom: 'He takes after your family, Bessy' (page 10). What do you think Mr Tulliver thinks of his wife's family?

5 How does Maggie confirm her parents' description of her when we meet her for the first time?

Forecasting

When we read we have an idea of what will happen. We predict what will happen in the short-term (next sentence or phrase); medium-term (next paragraph or page); long-term (next chapter). This is part of our understanding a text. We actively participate in creating meaning by using **our knowledge of the language** and **our knowledge of the world**.

Here are some general hints for your reading narrative writing in English:

- See how the book is organised: titles, chapters.
- Use the comprehension and anticipation exercises as a help before you read a chapter.
- Read each chapter the first time without checking every word you do not understand. Try and connect the plot and themes presented with what you already know.
- Grade vocabulary. What does it mean to say: 'I don't understand this word'? You can probably deduce its sense. Check the meaning of vocabulary which you think 'blocks' meaning. Find the equivalent in your language and then find out more about the word in an English learner's dictionary.
- Make predictions!

To help us interact with a text and make predictions a writer can do two things:

- Tell us explicitly about the development of the plot e.g. in chapter 1 Mr Tulliver tells us he intends to send his son to a good school.
- Leave less explicit hints, such as in chapter 1 when Mr Tulliver says 'It's no problem while she's little, but when she grows up she'll have trouble finding a husband'.

Keep track of these as you read each chapter. Sometimes you will be asked about them in the exercises.

CHAPTER 2

Tom comes home

Maggie sat in the attic, hugging [1] her doll and thinking about Tom. She was very excited because Tom was coming home from the Academy. She missed him when he was away at school and always counted the days until he would come home for the holidays. Now that he was coming home, they would have lots of fun. They would go fishing. They would take long walks along the river. There was only one thing that spoiled [2] her happiness: she was worried about the rabbits. Tom had told her to take care of his rabbits while he was away, but she had forgotten, and the rabbits had died. How could she tell Tom? He would be so angry.

Just then she heard the sound of the carriage coming. She threw her doll on the floor and ran out to meet Tom. Her mother and father were already outside. As soon as Tom got out of the carriage, Mrs Tulliver threw her arms around his neck and cried, 'There he is, my sweet boy!' Then Maggie gave him such a tight hug that his face went pink.

'Hello, Mother! Hello, Maggie!' said Tom.

Mr Tulliver shook Tom's hand, and they all went in for lunch. Mrs Tulliver had prepared Tom's favourite dishes. As soon as lunch was over, Tom turned to his sister and said, 'Let's go, Magsie!' (He only called her that when he was feeling very affectionate.)

Maggie jumped up, delighted to go anywhere with Tom, and, holding hands, they ran out of the house. They ran through the fields

1. **hugging** : with her arms around in a warm embrace.
2. **spoiled** : (here) ruined.

together, climbing over fences and splashing through the mud. As they passed by a tree, they heard a voice calling to them from high up among the branches. Looking up, they saw Bob Jakin, a local boy, with curly red hair, blue eyes, and freckles. ¹ Bob had a bird's egg in his hand. 'Hello, Bob!' called Tom, 'What have you got there?' Bob climbed down the tree and showed the bird's egg to Tom. Tom liked playing with Bob, because Bob knew all sorts of interesting things: he could recognise the different kinds of birds' eggs, and he knew where all the wasps' nests were. Maggie felt sure that Bob was wicked, ² perhaps even slightly diabolical. His mother was a large, fat woman who lived in a strange round house by the river. Maggie thought that house was probably full of bats and snakes. Whenever Tom and Maggie passed by, a dog ran out of the house and barked ³ at them. Once Bob's mother had shouted at them, telling them not to be frightened of the dog, but Maggie had thought that she was angry with them, and her heart had beaten with terror.

When he had finished looking at the bird's egg Tom said, 'Well, good-bye, Bob. Come on, Maggie. Let's go to see the rabbits. I hope you took good care of them.'

Maggie looked up at Tom's face anxiously. 'Please don't be angry with me, Tom,' she said.

'What do you mean? What's happened to the rabbits?' he demanded in an angry voice.

'I'm sorry, Tom. I just forgot about them, and now they're all dead.'

Tom's face went red with anger. 'I don't love you, Maggie!' he cried.

'Oh Tom, don't say that,' begged Maggie. 'I'm sorry. It was an accident, Tom. Please forgive me.'

---

1. **freckles** : small, pale brown marks on face.
2. **wicked** [wɪkɪd] : evil.
3. **barked** : made a loud noise typical of dogs.

'No, I won't forgive you. You're a naughty girl. Just go away and leave me alone!'

Maggie ran back into the house and up to the attic, sobbing pitifully. She sat on the floor, hugged her poor, battered [1] old doll and cried and cried. I'll never go downstairs again, she thought. I'll just stay up here and starve myself to death, and then he'll be sorry that he said he didn't love me!

Tom soon forgot about Maggie and their argument. He played in the fields and threw stones into the river until it was time for tea.

'Ah! There you are, my boy!' said Mrs Tulliver when Tom came in. 'Sit down and have a nice cake with your tea. But where is Maggie?'

'I don't know,' said Tom, choosing a big slice of cake with lots of cream on it.

'What?' said Mr Tulliver sharply. 'I thought she was playing with you. She's been looking forward so much to you coming home.'

'I haven't seen her for hours,' said Tom.

'Oh dear! I knew it! She's fallen into the river and drowned!' cried Mrs Tulliver, rushing to the window.

'Nonsense!' said Mr Tulliver. 'I bet Tom has been nasty [2] to her.'

'No I haven't. I think she's somewhere in the house.'

'Perhaps she's in the attic,' said Mrs Tulliver.

'Well, go and tell her tea is ready,' said Mr Tulliver to Tom. 'And be nice to her, or I'll be angry with you.'

Tom went off to the attic, holding his piece of cake. He did not want to go, but he never disobeyed his father. Maggie had been naughty, and Tom wanted to punish her. He was only thirteen years old, and he did not have very clear ideas about anything except this: if you do something wrong you should be punished. If he did anything wrong himself, he would not mind being punished for it,

---

1. **battered** : damaged.
2. **nasty** : not nice.

but he never did anything wrong.

When Maggie heard Tom's step on the stairs, she jumped up and wiped her tear-stained face. 'Please forgive me!' she said. 'I'll be good, I promise. I'll never forget anything again. Please love me, dear Tom.'

When we are older, we keep apart when we have quarrelled. But Maggie and Tom were very young. They were more like little animals than members of a civilised society. So Maggie hugged Tom and kissed his ear, and Tom forgot about punishing her and kissed her too.

'Don't cry, Magsie,' he said, taking her hand. 'Have some of my cake, and we'll go down for tea.'

A C T I V I T I E S

1 What does the rabbit incident tell you about Maggie?

2 'He was only thirteen years old, and he did not have very clear ideas about anything except this: if you do something wrong you should be punished.' What does this tell you about Tom?

3 Maggie and Tom are very different but as children they are close. Future problems are hinted at. Where?

4 In the next chapter we meet Mrs Tulliver's relatives. What do you think they will be like?

CHAPTER 3

The aunts and uncles are coming

The following Sunday, Mrs Tulliver baked her best cakes, because the aunts and uncles were coming. 'My sister Mrs Glegg just loves these cakes,' she said, setting the plates on the table. Mr Tulliver, who was sitting by the fire, did not reply.

'I wish that Maggie and Tom would be better behaved [1] when their aunts and uncles come,' said Mrs Tulliver. 'My sister Glegg has a lot of money and no children of her own. She might leave our children a nice sum of money when she dies. But Maggie is always so naughty and messy-looking, and Tom pays no attention to his aunt.'

'Don't be silly, Bessy,' said Mr Tulliver. 'Of course your sister will leave some money to our children, whether they're well behaved or not. Family is family.'

'But she might leave more money to Lucy. She's very fond of Lucy, and it's not surprising. I never saw a prettier little girl, and she's so good! You can sit her on a stool, [2] and she'll stay there for an hour!'

'Your sister Glegg will leave her money equally to her nieces and nephew, don't you worry. That's the respectable thing to do, and she would never do anything that was not respectable,' replied Mr Tulliver sarcastically.

Mrs Tulliver did not notice the sarcasm. 'Oh, yes! My sister Glegg is very respectable. My whole family is very respectable. The Dodsons have always been decent people. We go to church, and we dress nicely. Our houses are clean and tidy. And, when we die, we

---

1. **would be better behaved** : (here) would be good children.
2. **stool** : chair without back support.

always leave a good sum of money to our children and a little for our nieces and nephews too.'

Mr Tulliver, whose family was not quite so respectable, did not reply.

'Listen!' said Mrs Tulliver. 'Is that the carriage? Tom! Maggie! Come downstairs. Your aunts and uncles are here!'

There was a sharp knock on the door, and in walked Mrs Glegg, a large, handsome woman of fifty. After her came Mr Glegg, a plump, cheerful man who was a little shorter than his wife. Then came Mrs Deane, who was thin and pale, not so handsome as her sisters. Mr Deane came last, holding Lucy by the hand.

'Oh, how lovely to see you, Sisters!' cried Mrs Tulliver. 'Do come and sit down and have a cake. I've been baking all morning, and I believe these are the lightest, tastiest cakes I've ever baked.'

'No wonder you have money troubles,' said Mrs Glegg, sitting in the best chair and taking a cake. 'Here you are wasting good eggs and cream to make fancy cakes, when plain bread and butter would do just as well.'

Tom and Maggie ran downstairs and into the drawing room. [1] 'Good Lord!' said Mrs Glegg. 'What a noise you make! And aren't you going to say hello to your aunts and uncles? What rude little children you are!'

Tom and Maggie came forward shyly and said hello to their aunt. Then they went to stand by Lucy. Lucy was wearing her best clothes, and her blonde hair was curled prettily around her face. Standing there by Lucy, Maggie looked like a shaggy black puppy [2] beside a white kitten.

'Maggie,' said Mrs Tulliver. 'Go and brush your hair. I told you to brush it before you came downstairs.'

'I wasn't going to say anything, Sister, but the girl's hair does look

---

1. **drawing room** : room in a house where people relax and receive guests.
2. **shaggy ... puppy** : young dog with untidy hair.

a mess,' said Mrs Glegg, frowning [1] at Maggie. 'Perhaps you should tie it up with ribbons to keep it out of her face. What do you think, sister Deane?'

'I don't know, I'm sure,' said Mrs Deane complacently, stroking [2] her own daughter's tidy curls.

'Come upstairs with me, Tom,' whispered Maggie.

Tom followed Maggie, glad to get away from his aunts and uncles. In her mother's bedroom, Maggie opened the drawer and took out a large pair of scissors. She took hold of a great bunch of her hair and cut it off. 'Oh Lord!' cried Tom. 'Oh Maggie, you are going to get into such trouble!'

'I don't care,' said Maggie. 'I'm tired of them always talking about my hair. Help me to cut it, Tom.'

Tom took the scissors and cut off the rest of Maggie's hair. 'Look at yourself in the mirror,' he said, laughing. 'How funny you look!'

Maggie's eyes filled with tears as she looked at herself in the mirror. 'Don't laugh at me,' she cried angrily.

'Well, I'm going downstairs. You have only yourself to blame, Maggie, if you look like an idiot now. It wasn't my idea to cut your hair, so don't get angry with me.' And off he went, leaving Maggie in tears amid the heaps of black hair on the floor.

Ten minutes later, Maggie walked into the drawing room. A shocked silence greeted her appearance. Mrs Glegg was the first to recover. 'You should be ashamed of yourself, Maggie,' she said. 'Little girls who cut their own hair deserve to be punished.'

'Oh yes!' said Mr Glegg, trying to make a joke of it. 'We'll send you to prison, Maggie!'

'Oh Lord!' said Mrs Tulliver. 'She looks more like a gypsy than ever!'

'Don't cry, Maggie,' said Mr Tulliver. 'Come and sit by me.'

---

1. **frowning** [fraʊnɪŋ] : looking in a disapproving way.
2. **stroking** : caressing.

Maggie felt so grateful for her father's sympathy. She never forgot these times when her father comforted her, while everyone else was finding fault with her.

1 Check the meaning and pronunciation of the following words. Which of these do you associate with Mrs Tulliver's family?

> spontaneous   generous   conscientious   law-abiding   romantic
> hypocritical   thrifty   passionate   dishonest

2 What is the purpose for the development of the story of the Dodsons' visit?

3 Are all the members of the family the same?

4 What does the hair-cutting incident tell you about Maggie and Tom?

5 **Functions**

Look at these examples: 'Congratulations!', 'Well done!', 'You must be so happy', 'I'd like to take this opportunity to congratulate you', 'Nice one!'. The style varies but the speakers of each of these phrases are doing the same thing, **congratulating**. When Mr Tulliver says to his daughter at the end of the chapter: 'Don't cry Maggie. Come and sit by me', he is **consoling**. These are called functions. When we speak we are performing some form of **function**: apologising, making excuses, expressing regret, etc. Look at Mrs Glegg's language in chapter 3. What is she doing?

6 Look at the title of the next chapter. What do you imagine Maggie did? Compare your answers in a group.

CHAPTER 4

Maggie behaves worse than she expected

After tea, Maggie, Tom and Lucy went out to play. As they walked along, Tom giggled [1] every time he looked at Maggie's hair. 'Oh dear! I can't help it, Maggie. You look so funny,' he said. Maggie pushed him angrily. 'Hey!' said Tom. 'You *do* have a bad temper, Maggie. Not like Lucy. Lucy would never push anyone, would you?'

'I don't think I would,' said Lucy, shyly.

'I wish Lucy was my sister instead of you,' said Tom.

'That's very cruel of you,' said Maggie, trying to keep back the tears.

'Come on, Lucy,' said Tom. 'Let's go and look at the toads [2] in the pond.'

'Isn't it very muddy by the pond?' asked Lucy. 'I don't want to get my dress dirty. And what about Maggie? Doesn't Maggie want to come and see the toads too?'

'Maggie's in a bad mood,' said Tom. 'She doesn't want to come. And don't worry about the mud. Your dress will be all right.'

Tom and Lucy ran ahead towards the pond, holding hands. Maggie felt angry, hurt and jealous. She felt as if small demons had taken possession of her soul. Standing by a tree, she watched Tom and Lucy as they bent over the pond with their heads close together. Once in a while Lucy looked over anxiously, and finally she cried,

---

1. **giggled** [gɪgəld] : laughed in a silly way.
2. **toads** : animals like frogs that live on land but breed in water.

'Maggie! Maggie! Do come here. There is such a funny big toad! Do come and see.'

Maggie walked slowly over to the pond but, when she reached Lucy's side, Tom looked up with a frown and said, 'What are you here for? Go away!'

Suddenly all the pain and anger she had been feeling ever since the aunts and uncles arrived swelled up in Maggie, and she pushed Lucy hard. Lucy fell forward into the mud and burst into tears.

Tom leapt up and slapped [1] Maggie's arm. 'Why did you do that?' he cried angrily. Then he went to help Lucy out of the mud. Maggie went back to her tree and watched them as they returned to the house. She did not feel sorry for what she had done. Usually she felt sorry as soon as she had done something wrong, but now Tom and Lucy had made her feel so miserable [2] that she was glad to spoil their happiness.

Meanwhile, in the drawing room, Mr Tulliver had been discussing Tom's education with the aunts and uncles.

'Mr Riley told me about a good school not far away. The school master is a man called Stelling. He is a clergyman and has a degree from the University. Riley says that Lawyer Wakem's son goes to Stelling's school, so it must be good.'

'But Lawyer Wakem's son is a hunchback,' [3] said Mrs Deane.

'What's that got to do with it?' asked Mr Tulliver impatiently. 'The point is that Lawyer Wakem is the cleverest, meanest, [4] nastiest lawyer in St Ogg's, and if he sends his son to Stelling's school you can be sure that it is the best school around. I'll be glad for Tom to go to school with Wakem's son. That way he will learn how fellows [5] like Wakem think. He will be able to argue with them and prove them

1. **slapped** : hit.
2. **miserable** : sad.
3. **hunchback** : person whose back is abnormally curved.
4. **meanest** : most ungenerous.
5. **fellows** : men.

wrong and help me in all these lawsuits.'

'Well, Mr Tulliver,' said Mrs Glegg. 'I always said you shouldn't get into these lawsuits to begin with. They are a waste of money, and the Lord knows you don't have money to waste!'

'Don't you worry about my money, Mrs Glegg,' said Mr Tulliver. 'That's my business, not yours! Of course I have to get into lawsuits. Take this business of the dam, 1 for example. This man Pivart, who owns the property just up the river from mine, wants to build a dam. But if he builds a dam, there will be less water to power my mill! I can't let that happen! And the only way to fight it is to go to court.'

'But what if you lose the lawsuit?' asked Mrs Glegg. 'Then you will have to pay all the expenses, and they will still build the dam! And if you send Tom to this new school, that will cost a fortune too. Where will you get the money from, Mr Tulliver?'

'There you go again, Mrs Glegg!' said Mr Tulliver, raising his voice. 'What I do with my own money is my business! And I won't have an interfering woman tell me what to do in my own house!'

'Interfering woman?' cried Mrs Glegg, becoming red in the face. 'You dare to call me an interfering woman? Why, it's lucky for you I interfered and lent you five hundred pounds when you lost the last lawsuit!'

'You'll get your money back, Mrs Glegg, if that's what's worrying you!'

'Come, come,' said Mr Glegg in a cheerful voice. 'Let's not quarrel.'

'Are you taking his part against your own wife, Mr Glegg?' asked Mrs Glegg, furious.

'No, Jane, of course not,' said poor Mr Glegg. 'I was just trying to make peace, that's all.'

'Well I'm not going to sit here and be insulted,' said Mrs Glegg,

---

1. **dam** : barrier built across a river to hold the water back.

rising from her chair and putting on her gloves. 'I'm going home.'

'Oh dear! Don't go, Sister,' cried Mrs Tulliver.

'Let her go, Bessy,' said Mr Tulliver, 'if that's what she wants to do.'

Just then the door opened and Mrs Deane let out a scream. Standing in the doorway were Tom and Lucy. Lucy was crying, and her pretty dress and hair were all covered in mud.

A C T I V I T I E S

1 Are the following statements true or false? Correct those that are false.

		True	False
a	Lucy made fun of Maggie's hair.	☐	☐
b	Maggie was sorry she had pushed Lucy into the mud.	☐	☐
c	Mr Tulliver wants Tom to make friends with Wakem's son.	☐	☐
d	Mrs Glegg decides to leave.	☐	☐

2 In chapter 1 we saw how predicting what happens is an essential part of constructing meaning when we read. A writer can tell the reader what will happen or give hints. There is an example of both in chapter 4. Find them and discuss their possible importance in the story.

3 The title of the next chapter tells us what Maggie will do next. What do you think her visit to the gypsies will be like?

4 Go back to the argument between Mr Tulliver and Mrs Glegg. What do you think are the strong and weak points of their respective arguments? In pairs, one of you must defend Mr Tulliver whilst the other defends Mrs Glegg.

CHAPTER 5

Maggie runs away to the gypsies

As Tom and Lucy disappeared from sight, Maggie decided she would not go home. No! She would run away to the gypsies, and Tom would never see her again. She was used to her mother and her aunts saying that she looked like a gypsy. Surely the gypsies would welcome her and treat her with respect.

She knew there were gypsies on Dunlow Common, and so she set off in that direction, walking fast. When she had crossed three wide fields she slowed down, because walking fast had made her tired, and she suddenly realised that she was very hungry too. Running away was not as easy as she had imagined. It seemed a very long way to Dunlow Common.

By the time she got there, Maggie was so tired and hungry that she felt like crying again, but when she saw the gypsies' tents and the smoke rising from their fire she felt a little better. A tall young woman with a baby in her arms was standing by the fire. She watched with interest as Maggie approached.

'Where are you going to, my little lady?' asked the young woman.

'I'm coming to stay with you, if you don't mind,' Maggie replied. Looking up at the young woman's face, Maggie had to agree with her mother and aunts. With her dark eyes, dark hair, and brown skin, the young woman looked very much like Maggie, except that she was grown up and rather dirty.

'Come to stay with us? How nice. Come on, then,' said the young woman, taking Maggie's hand.

Several other gypsies were sitting around the fire. Maggie's new friend took her to an old gypsy-woman who was stirring [1] a pot of soup. Two dirty children were lying on the ground beside her and, not far away, a girl was giving hay to a donkey. They looked very nice in the evening light, Maggie thought. Once she had taught them to wash themselves and read books, they would be delightful companions.

The young woman spoke to the old one in a strange language. At last, the old woman said, 'So, my pretty lady, you have come to stay with us, have you? Sit down and tell us where you come from.'

'I've run away from home, because I was unhappy there,' said Maggie. 'I want to be a gypsy and live with you. I can teach you a lot of interesting things. Do you have a queen? If not, maybe I could be your queen when I grow up.'

'Such a clever little lady,' said the young woman. 'And what pretty clothes you have!'

'Tell me,' said the old woman, handing Maggie a bowl of soup. 'Is your family very rich? Do you live in a big house?'

'I live at Dorlcote Mill, but I don't want to go back there.' Maggie tasted the soup. She was very hungry, but she did not like the taste of it. 'Could I please have some bread and butter and tea instead?' she asked.

'We don't have any butter,' said the old woman sharply. Just then, two men and a black dog came up to the fire. The men spoke to the old woman in their strange language and stared at Maggie. The dog started growling [2] and barking at her. The young woman handed something to one of the men, and he looked at it closely by the light of the fire. Maggie realised with a shock that it was her own silver thimble. [3] It had been in her pocket. When had they taken it, and how, and why? Maggie felt suddenly lonely and lost. The gypsies did

---

1. **stirring** : mixing with a spoon.
2. **growling** : making a low threatening sound.
3. **thimble** : small cap of metal worn on the thumb while sewing.

not look so nice and friendly now; in fact, they were rather frightening. Had they stolen her thimble, or would the man give it back to her? Maggie tried to keep the tears back. She began to think that the gypsies might kill her. Oh, where was her father! She wished so much that he would come and save her.

'I must go now,' said Maggie suddenly, standing up. 'It's getting dark, and I had better go home. I will come and see you again another day and bring you some nice food.'

But the old gypsy-woman said, 'Don't go! Stay with us a while, little lady. Then we will take you home.'

Maggie sat down again, sure that the gypsies meant to keep her. But after they had finished eating, one of the men brought the donkey over to Maggie and said, 'Come on, then. I'll take you home.' He lifted her up and put her on the donkey, and then he climbed on behind her.

'Won't you come too?' Maggie asked the young woman. She was frightened of being alone with the gypsy-man. But the young woman shook her head and waved good-bye, and the donkey started off into the darkness.

Maggie had never been so afraid in all her life as she was then, riding along the shadowy lane with the gypsy-man behind her. After a long while, she saw a sign that read, 'St Ogg's 2 miles'. Perhaps the gypsy-man really meant to take her home! Perhaps he didn't mean to kill her after all! Perhaps he was a good man, even though he had not returned her thimble. Then suddenly she saw a trap [1] coming towards them. She recognised the white-faced horse and cried out, 'Oh! It is my father! Please stop!'

Maggie jumped down from the donkey just as her father was climbing out of the trap. She ran to him and threw her arms around his neck, sobbing with relief.

'There, there, poor little girl,' said Mr Tulliver, hugging her

---

1. **trap** : small, two-wheeled, horse-drawn carriage.

tightly. 'Where on earth [1] have you been?'

'She got lost,' said the gypsy-man. 'I was just bringing her home.'

'Thank you. I've been so worried about her,' said Mr Tulliver, and he gave the gypsy-man five shillings. [2]

In the trap, Mr Tulliver held the reins in one hand and put his other arm around Maggie. 'Now, tell me what happened,' he said.

'Tom was nasty to me and made me miserable, so I ran away.'

'Oh, you mustn't do that, little girl,' said Mr Tulliver. 'What would I do without you?'

---

1. **on earth** : ever.
2. **shillings** : units of money used in Britain until 1971.

A   C   T   I   V   I   T   I   E   S

1 The gypsies in reality were different from how Maggie had imagined them. Find the differences.

2 What does Maggie's reunion with her father tell you about their relationship?

3 In chapter 6 Tom attends Mr Stelling's school. What problems do you think he will have?

Tom's new school

Tom was unhappy at Mr Stelling's school. At his old school, sports had been very important, and Tom was good at sports, so he had been liked and respected by the other boys. But sports were not important at Mr Stelling's school. Here the only thing that mattered was school work, and Tom was not very good at Latin or Euclid. For the first time in his life, Tom felt that he was not good enough, and that other boys were better than he.

Mr Stelling was convinced that Latin and Euclid were the only things worth learning, and that learning these things would bring out the best in any boy. He soon decided that Tom Tulliver was a very stupid boy indeed and began to make jokes at Tom's expense at the dinner table, where all the other boys could hear.

In this miserable situation, Tom became more like a girl than he had ever been before. At the Academy, Tom had been proud of himself and full of boyish self-confidence. Here, he felt vulnerable, like a girl. He wished very much that he could do well in his studies and please Mr Stelling, so that Mr Stelling would respect him, but no matter how hard he tried he could not remember the genders of Latin nouns and he could not understand Euclid. Sometimes, when he was trying to study, he felt tears come into his eyes, and he wiped them away quickly so that no one would see them.

He missed Maggie very much. He had never missed her when he was at the Academy, but now he would give anything to have Maggie by his side, to walk by the river with her or go fishing with her.

Towards the end of Tom's first academic term at Stelling's, Mrs Stelling invited Maggie to visit the school for two weeks. Mr Tulliver brought Maggie to the school in the trap.

'Magsie!' cried Tom, running out to meet her.

Maggie was pleased and surprised at this warm welcome and hugged him tightly.

'Hello, Father,' said Tom. 'Won't you come and have tea with Mr Stelling before riding home?'

'No, no. I want to get back before dark. How are your studies going, Tom?'

'I'm afraid they are not going very well, Father.'

'And why is that? You must do what your master tells you.'

'I try,' said Tom, 'but I can't seem to learn things properly.'

'I'll help you now,' said Maggie.

'How can you help me, silly? Girls can't do Latin. I'll show you one of my school books, and then you'll see how difficult it is.'

'I know what Latin is,' said Maggie. 'It's a language. There are Latin words in the dictionary, like "bonus", a gift.'

'Well done, little girl!' cried Mr Tulliver with delight.

'You're wrong, Maggie. "Bonus" means "good",' said Tom.

When Mr Tulliver had gone, Tom took Maggie to the study room and showed her his school books. He was glad to see that Maggie could not understand Euclid at all, but when they looked at the Latin grammar she became quite interested.

That evening at dinner Maggie chatted [1] to Mr Stelling, and it was clear that the school master found her interesting and clever. Tom was surprised to see that Maggie was not at all afraid of Mr Stelling.

'And what do you think of your brother's school books, young lady?' asked Mr Stelling with a smile.

'I like the Latin grammar,' said Maggie. 'I don't understand the Euclid, but I'm sure I would, if I spent a lot of time on it.'

'No, you wouldn't,' said Tom. 'Girls can't do Euclid, can they, Mr Stelling?'

---

1. **chatted** : talked.

'They can learn a little of everything,' said Mr Stelling. 'They have a great deal of superficial cleverness, but they couldn't go far into anything. They're quick and shallow.'[1]

Tom was delighted with Mr Stelling's reply, but Maggie was very upset by it. All her life, her father had called her 'quick', and she had felt proud of it. But now, it seemed, her quickness was something that made her inferior. It would have been better to be slow, like Tom.

---

1. **shallow** : superficial.

1 Complete the table comparing Tom's old school with Mr Stelling's.

Tom's old school	Mr Stelling's school
a Sports were important	**a**
b	**b** Tom couldn't understand Latin and Euclid
c Tom was popular with other boys	**c**
d	**d** He felt vulnerable and miserable

2 There are high points and low points for the Tulliver children in this chapter. Complete the table below.

Tom		Maggie	
High points	Low points	High points	Low points
a	**b**	**a**	**b**
c	**d**	**c**	**d**

3 In the next chapter Maggie meets Lawyer Wakem's son, Philip. Can you predict why they will become friends?

CHAPTER 7

A love scene

The next day, when Tom and Maggie went into the study room, one of Tom's fellow-students was there, reading a book. The boy was terribly deformed. His body was small and crooked, [1] and he had a hump [2] on his back. But his face was rather beautiful. He had large grey eyes and pale skin and curly light brown hair.

'Hello, Philip,' said Tom. 'Maggie, this is Philip Wakem. Philip, this is my sister Maggie.'

Tom opened a book and started to read it, not because he wanted to study but because he did not like to look at Philip: he found it embarrassing. Tom had a vague idea that Philip's deformity was Lawyer Wakem's punishment for being such a bad man. Tom's father always said that Lawyer Wakem was the meanest lawyer in St Ogg's and that he used all his cleverness to rob decent people of their rights.

Philip knew that Tom did not like to look at him, and this made Philip feel very bitter. Nobody liked to look at him, but he hated it even more in this tall, healthy, handsome, active boy. Philip had noticed that Tom was not very clever, and this gave him a bitter pleasure.

'Hello,' said Maggie, walking up to Philip.

Unlike Tom, Maggie looked at Philip with great interest. She had always felt a tenderness for deformed things. There was a deformed lamb among the sheep in the field by Dorlcote Mill, and Maggie

---

1. **crooked** [krʊkɪd] : not straight.
2. **hump** : round projecting part.

always loved to caress it. She felt that the deformed lamb would like being caressed more than the healthy lambs did, and she wanted her affection to be appreciated. She loved Tom very much, but she often wished that he cared more about her loving him.

During the two weeks that Maggie stayed at Stelling's school, she spent a lot of time with Philip Wakem. They talked about music and books and other things that did not interest Tom. One day, Maggie found Philip reading in the garden.

'What are you reading?' she asked.

'It's the story of Philoctetes,' said Philip, blushing [1] a little.

'Would you tell me the story?' asked Maggie.

'All right,' said Philip, and he told her the story of the Greek hero Philoctetes, who had a very bad wound in his foot. 'He cried so much because of the pain that his friends couldn't stand it, so they left him alone on an island...'

Philip thought that Maggie was very nice, much nicer than her brother. Her dark eyes reminded him of a fairy story in which a princess was turned into an animal. He enjoyed his talks with her a great deal and was beginning to be very fond of her.

'Did Philoctetes have a sister?' asked Maggie.

'I don't really know. I don't think so.'

'Because if he had a sister, she would have gone to the island with him and taken care of him.'

'Would she?' asked Philip, looking at Maggie with his gentle grey eyes. 'I wish I had a sister. Maggie, if you had a brother like me, do you think you would love him as much as you love Tom?'

'Oh yes. I would probably love him even more,' she said impetuously. Then she thought a little and said, 'Well, no, I don't think I could love anyone more than I love Tom. But I'm very fond of you, and I wish you were my brother too. You are so clever, and you can play the piano and sing.'

---

1. **blushing** : going slightly red due to emotion.

'But soon you will go away, and then you will forget about me,' said Philip.

'No, I won't, Philip. I think we will always be friends.'

'I hope so.'

'Why, Philip, I think you're fonder of me than Tom is,' said Maggie, rather sadly. 'Would you like me to kiss you, as I do Tom?'

'Yes, very much: nobody kisses me.'

Maggie kissed Philip with great tenderness. 'There!' she said. 'Now we will always be friends, and I will kiss you every time we meet.'

A   C   T   I   V   I   T   I   E   S

1 What different feelings does Tom have towards Philip?

2 Philip's deformity hides a sensitive and intelligent boy. Find the things Maggie likes about him.

3 'She had always felt a tenderness for deformed things.' What does this tell you about Maggie?

4 Maggie says: 'I think we will always be friends'. Why could this be a problem for both of them in the future?

5 The Pivart lawsuit is important in the next chapter. Can you remember what it was? (See chapter 4.)

CHAPTER ◆ 8

The golden gates are passed

The years passed, and Tom went on at Stelling's school, while Maggie went to Miss Firniss's school with her cousin Lucy. Maggie sometimes visited Tom at Stelling's, and she often wrote him letters. At the end of each letter, she told him to send her love to Philip. In his replies, Tom hardly ever mentioned Philip. They had never been friends. Now that Mr Tulliver was involved in a big lawsuit against Pivart, and Mr Wakem was acting as Pivart's lawyer, Tom felt it was not right to be friendly with Philip. Even Maggie saw that it was difficult to be friends with Philip now. Her father got angry every time he heard the name Wakem, and he had told Tom to stay away from Philip at school.

One day, Mr Stelling came into the study room and told Tom that his sister had come to see him; she was waiting for him in the drawing room. Tom was surprised. He had not been expecting Maggie. When he opened the drawing room door, Maggie came over and kissed him. Tom was now nearly seventeen years old, and Maggie was thirteen. They were both tall and good-looking. Maggie looked very beautiful. But today her dark eyes looked sad and anxious.

'Maggie! What are you doing here? Did Father bring you?'

'No. I came by the coach and walked here from the village.'

'But why aren't you in school?'

'Father wanted me at home,' said Maggie.

'Is something wrong?'

'Oh, Tom! The lawsuit has ended and Father has lost! He will lose the mill and the land and everything! There will be nothing left!'

Tom turned pale and sat down. He had never worried about the future or about money. His father had always seemed to have plenty. But now his father would lose everything. He would go bankrupt, and Tom knew that that was a terrible disgrace.

'Shall I come home with you, Maggie?' he said at last.

'Yes. Mother would like you to come, and things are so dreadful at home now. And Father... poor Father...'

'What is it, Maggie?'

'He fell off his horse, and he has been very strange ever since. He seems to have lost his senses... He lies in bed and doesn't recognise Mother when she comes into the room. I'm the only person he recognises now. We must go. He'll miss me.'

Tom told Mr Stelling what had happened, then he and Maggie walked to the village to take the coach. They had left the Garden of Eden and were entering a new life of sorrow. The golden gates of their childhood had closed forever behind them.

A C T I V I T I E S

1 Why did Tom stay away from Philip?

2 How did Mr Tulliver react to the news of the loss of the lawsuit?

3 How is their childhood portrayed?

4 Can you give another title to the chapter? Compare your title with other members of your class. Which one do you prefer?

PART 1

1 Read the text below and notice what type of words are missing. Now read the adjectives listed below. Check their meaning. Complete this description of the principal characters introduced in part 1 with the appropriate adjectives from the list below. There are various possibilities for Mr Tulliver!

Mr and Mrs Tulliver and their two children, Tom and Maggie, live at Dorlcote Mill near the town of St. Ogg's on the River Floss. Mr Tulliver is a ᵃ......................., ᵇ....................... man who is always losing lawsuits of his own seeking. His wife is a Dodson and often the object of censure from her sisters for having married someone ᶜ....................... and ᵈ....................... . Mr Tulliver regards the Dodsons as a ᵉ......................., ᶠ....................... lot. Maggie and Tom are very different. Tom is an ᵍ....................... character who has a strong sense of what is right and wrong. This can lead him to being ʰ....................... and ⁱ....................... . He is proud of his physical strength but is not particularly ʲ......................., as his father suspects. Maggie, with her ᵏ....................... hair and ˡ....................... skin, is an ᵐ....................... girl. She can never keep herself ⁿ....................... and loves to wander near the river. She is ᵒ....................... and reads books normally read by adults.

> argumentative bright brown cold dark hard
> hot-tempered impulsive intelligent proud rash selfish
> tidy unforgiving upright

2 Put these events from part 1 into their correct order. **Two** should not be there!

a ☐ Maggie meets Philip Wakem.

b ☐ Maggie cuts off her hair.

c ☐ Maggie runs away to the gypsies.

d ☐ Mr Tulliver loses the Pivart lawsuit and is ruined.

e ☐ Mrs Tulliver's sisters and their husbands come for Sunday tea.

f ☐ Maggie forgets to look after Tom's rabbits.

g ☐ Maggie visits Tom at Mr Stelling's school.

h ☐ Tom fights with Philip.

i ☐ Tom returns from school.

j ☐ Tom is sent to Mr Stelling's school.

k ☐ Tom is very angry with Maggie.

l ☐ Tom is forced to leave Mr Stelling's school.

m ☐ Mr Tulliver punishes Maggie.

n ☐ Maggie pushes Lucy into the mud.

3 Now use the sentences to write a summary of part 1. Use the present simple as in the text in chapter 3 describing the Tullivers and Dodsons.

4 Go back to chapter 6 exercises 1 and 2. Express the differences in two short texts. Use contrastive linking words such as *however, on the other hand,* etc..

5 Find a description of your town or city (or one nearby) in English. Look at the style and language used. Now write a description of St Ogg's for a tourist guide. Try and use the appropriate style. (150-180 words)

6 Have you got a brother or a sister? Are you an only child? Discuss the advantages and disadvantages with a partner.

7 Write **either** a description of your brother(s) or sister(s) and your relationship with them **or** a story entitled 'The day my brother arrived: the end to being an only child.' (150-180 words)

CHAPTER ◆ 9

What had happened at home

When Mr Tulliver found out that he had lost the lawsuit, he seemed to bear the disappointment very well. He was a proud man, and he did not want Wakem or anyone else to think that he had been crushed [1] by the blow. [2] He knew that the costs of the lawsuit were more than he could pay but, instead of despairing, he tried to think of ways to survive the disaster. For example, Mr Furley owned the mortgage [3] on the mill. He could sell the mill to Mr Furley on condition that Mr Furley let him continue to live there as a tenant. [4] That way Furley could keep the price of the mortgage, and Mr Tulliver could use the rest of the money to pay the costs of the lawsuit, without the humiliation of being forced to leave the mill. He was sure that Mr Furley would agree to this plan.

Unfortunately, he had borrowed five hundred pounds from Mr Dix – a prosperous businessman in St Ogg's – two months earlier, so that he could pay his debt to Mrs Glegg. At the time, he had been sure that he would win the lawsuit and have no trouble repaying Mr Dix, so he

---

1. **crushed** : destroyed.
2. **blow** : shock.
3. **mortgage** [mɔːrgɪdʒ] : agreement by which money is lent by a bank for buying a property.
4. **tenant** : person who pays rent to the owner for the use of a building or room.

had signed a paper saying that, if he could not pay, Mr Dix would get all his household furniture. Now he had no hope of paying the five hundred pounds, so Mr Dix would have the right to take everything in the mill, and leave them without a bed or a kitchen table. Mr Tulliver hated asking his wife's family for help, but it had to be done. He would send Bessy to talk to Mrs Glegg. He was sure that Mrs Glegg would not let Bessy's furniture be taken away.

These thoughts were running through his mind one evening as he rode home on horseback, when he met a messenger bearing a letter for him. The letter was from Mr Tulliver's lawyer, who had spoken to Mr Furley that day. With a flushed [1] face and shining eyes, Mr Tulliver opened the letter as the messenger rode away. It was a short message, but it took Mr Tulliver a long time to make sense of it. It said that Mr Furley, having money problems of his own, had sold Mr Tulliver's mortgage to – Wakem.

Half an hour later, a man riding by had found Mr Tulliver lying on the road, unconscious, with the letter gripped [2] in his hand. Mr Tulliver was taken home and put to bed. When he regained consciousness, he called Maggie's name, so Mrs Tulliver sent a message to Miss Firniss's school, asking Maggie to come home immediately.

When Maggie arrived, the doctor told her that her father had had an attack and had lost his memory. Maggie rushed up to her father's room and sat beside his bed. He seemed pleased to see her but could not speak. Mrs Tulliver was very upset. She kept bursting into tears and calling for Tom.

So the next day, as we have seen, Maggie went to Stelling's school to get Tom.

In the coach, on the way home, she explained about the letter that had caused all this sorrow.

1. **flushed** : red coloured due to emotion.
2. **gripped** : held tightly.

'So it is Wakem's fault,' said Tom, frowning. 'I believe that man has always wanted to ruin my father. When I am grown up, I will make him pay for it. You must never speak to Philip again, Maggie.'

When they got home, they found a strange man in the drawing room, sitting in Mr Tulliver's chair, smoking a pipe. 'Good afternoon,' he said, embarrassed by their startled [1] young faces.

Tom turned and walked quickly out of the room. Maggie followed him, whispering, 'Who is that?' Suddenly she was afraid that the man's presence had something to do with her father's illness, so she rushed upstairs, but Mr Tulliver was lying quietly in bed, with his eyes closed.

Maggie and Tom searched the house for Mrs Tulliver, but they could not find her. At last they found her in the little storage room where she kept all her best things. There sat Mrs Tulliver, surrounded by her best cups, saucers and plates, the ones she only used on very special occasions. The poor woman was shaking her head and weeping, hugging a silver teapot to her breast. 'Oh, Tom!' she cried, when she saw him. 'We're ruined! Everything will be sold... We shall be beggars! Even my best things will have to go, the things I wanted to leave to you one day, my boy, and to Maggie too, of course.'

'But, Mother!' said Tom. 'Will my aunts let all your things be sold? Have you asked them for help?'

---

1. **startled** : surprised.

'Yes, I have. But they say that I was foolish to marry your father and that your father was foolish to go to law, 1 and that now we are being punished for our foolishness. They say they will buy some of my best things at the auction, 2 so that they won't go to strangers. I've had to sit and watch while your father spent my fortune and what should have been your fortune too. I told him not to go to law, but he never listened to me, and now he has brought me to ruin!'

Tom put his arms around his mother and tried to comfort her. For the first time, he began to think that his father was to blame. It was his father's fault that a strange man was sitting in the drawing room. It was his father's fault that the whole family was now in disgrace, and people would talk about them with contempt. But he – Tom Tulliver – would behave like a man and take care of his mother.

Maggie, meanwhile, had listened to her mother's complaints with growing anger. How could her mother criticise her father, who was lying ill – perhaps dying – upstairs? What did it matter if the plates and the teapot had to be sold? Tom and her mother were thinking only of themselves. They were shutting Maggie out from 3 the family disaster. At last her anger burst out and she cried, 'Mother, how can you talk like that? As if you only cared about your things, when my father is ill and may never be able to speak to us again!' She left the room and ran upstairs to sit by her father's bed.

1. **to go to law** : resort to legal action to decide on a dispute.
2. **auction** : public sale where things are sold to the person who offers the most money for them.
3. **shutting Maggie out from** : excluding Maggie from.

1 Mr Tulliver's finances are complicated! Sort out the confusion present in these sentences. In each sentence ONE word is incorrect according to the story. Cross out the incorrect word and write the correct word in the space provided as in the example (0).

0 ~~Wakem~~ owes money to several people.   ....Mr.Tulliver....

a Mr Tulliver had a mortgage on the mill.   ....

b If Mr Furley bought the mortgage, the Tullivers could stay at the mill.   ....

c With the money from the furniture, Mr Tulliver could pay the costs of the Pivart lawsuit.   ....

d Mr Tulliver had borrowed £500 from Mr Furley to repay Mrs Glegg.   ....

e If Mr Tulliver didn't repay Mr Dix, Dix could take possession of the mill.   ....

f Furley had sold the mortgage to Mr Tulliver.   ....

2 Mr Tulliver's solutions always come up against obstacles, he thinks he has found a solution to his problems when some other problem comes up. Using the ideas present in the sentences you corrected in exercise 1, complete these sentences. Example: *'Although Mr Tulliver had lost the lawsuit, he thought he could sell the mill to Mr Furley.'*

a Although he did not have enough money to pay the costs of the lawsuit, ...

b He could get money by selling the mill to Mr Furley. However, ...

c He had been sure of winning the lawsuit and so paying back Mr Dix but ....

d He would ask his wife to speak to her family despite ....
....

3 Which word is different? Explain why.

   a teapot / cup / plate / saucer / letter
   b Furley / Dix / Glegg / Wakem
   c ruin / debt / disgrace / beggars / illness

4 Compare Maggie and Tom's reaction to the disaster.

5 'Wakem proves to be Mr Tulliver's nemesis.' (Nemesis: punishment or defeat that is deserved and cannot be avoided.) To what extent do you agree with this statement? Compare your ideas in a group.

6 Chapter 10 is entitled 'The family council'. We met Mrs Tulliver's family in chapters 3 and 4. What do you think the Deanes and the Gleggs will do in the next chapter?

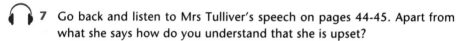 7 Go back and listen to Mrs Tulliver's speech on pages 44-45. Apart from what she says how do you understand that she is upset?

CHAPTER 10

The family council

At eleven the next morning, the aunts and uncles arrived for a family council. Mr Deane was not coming, because he was away for the day on business. He had been rising in the world as rapidly as Mr Tulliver had been falling, and now Mrs Deane arrived in a new carriage driven by a servant in an elegant uniform.

'Oh, Sister!' said Mrs Tulliver. 'What a disaster! We are truly ruined!'

Mrs Deane was a thin-lipped woman who made small speeches on special occasions then repeated them to her husband, asking him if he thought she had spoken well. 'Yes, Sister,' she said now. 'But troubles do not come without a cause. However, I'm very sorry for you, and if the doctor orders wine for Mr Tulliver, let me know. I'll send it willingly.'

Then Mr and Mrs Glegg arrived. 'Sister,' said Mrs Glegg in a severe voice, 'we have come to discuss what can be done about the disgrace that has fallen on our family and to see what we can do to save you and your children from poverty.'

'If only some of my best things could be saved and not put up for sale!'

'Don't be silly, Bessy,' said Mrs Glegg. 'You must think about your situation, not about your best things. What do they matter when the question is, will you have a bed to lie on? If you do, it will only be because we buy it for you. You are dependent upon us for everything now, because your husband lies helpless upstairs and hasn't got a penny in the world. I'm saying this for your own good, because you ought to know the situation you are in and the disgrace that your husband has brought upon your family.'

'Come, come,' said Mr Glegg, kindly, 'let's not make things too dark. What's done can't be undone. We will try to buy what you need, although – as Mrs Glegg says – they must be useful, plain things. A table and chairs, kitchen things, and a good bed.'

Just then, Tom and Maggie came into the drawing room.

'You should both hear what we have to say, Tom and Maggie,' said Mrs Glegg. 'We were just talking about what we can do to save you and your mother from poverty. You have no one but us to help you now, since your father has brought this disgrace upon you.'

When she heard this criticism of her father Maggie flushed, and her eyes lit up with anger but, just as she was about to speak, Tom put his hand on her arm and whispered, 'Be quiet, Maggie.' Then he turned to his aunt Glegg and spoke to her in a quiet and respectful manner: 'Aunt, if you think it is a disgrace to the family that the furniture will be sold, wouldn't it be better to prevent it? If you and my aunt Deane plan to leave any money to me and Maggie in your wills, [1] wouldn't it be better to give it to us now so that we can pay the debt, and my mother will not have to lose her furniture?'

There was silence for a few moments, for everyone, including Maggie, was astonished at Tom's sudden manliness [2] of tone. Uncle Glegg was the first to speak.

'Well done, young man!' he said. 'That is very sensible of you!'

'Mr Glegg!' cried his wife, angrily. 'It is my money you are talking about! Money I have saved so that I can leave a respectable will. I'm not going to give them money now and leave a poor will. Mine is a will I can be proud of, and I'm not changing it!'

This was too much for Maggie. She jumped up from the sofa, her

---

1. **wills** : legal documents stating to whom your possessions are to be given after your death.
2. **manliness** : maturity (he speaks like a grown man, not like a boy).

eyes flashing like the eyes of a young lioness. 'Why did you come, then?' she cried. 'Why are you talking and interfering with us, if you don't plan to help us, if you don't plan to help your own sister? Keep away from us, then! And don't criticise my father! He is better than any of you. He would have helped any of you, if you had been in trouble. Tom and I don't ever want to have your money, if you won't help my poor mother!'

Mrs Tulliver was frightened by this mad outburst. She did not see how life could go on after it. Tom was irritated: it was useless to talk like that. The aunts were silent in surprise for some moments. Then Mrs Glegg spoke: 'Bessy, I've always said that child would end badly. I'm not surprised. There's nothing of our family in her.'

'Come now,' said Mr Glegg. 'Let's get a pen and some paper. We're here to decide what to buy in the sale for this poor family. Let's calm down and do what we came to do.'

1 What do Mrs Tulliver's family (Mrs Deane, Mr and Mrs Glegg) do to help? Do you think it is enough?

2 What is your opinion of Mrs Glegg?

3 Who could say or think the following things? Write the name next to the sentence.

Sentence   **Speaker**

a The financial situation of the Tullivers is their   ....
   own fault.

b Let's try and make the best of a bad situation.   ....

c We must swallow our pride.   ....

d How dare they criticise!   ....

4 In chapter 11, Tom starts work with Mr Deane. He will start from the bottom. What progress do you expect him to make?

Tom looks for work

The next morning, at ten o'clock, Tom went to St Ogg's to see his uncle Deane. He was a proud boy, and he felt the humiliation of his situation as well as the difficulty of it. He would ask no one to help him. He knew that both his uncle Glegg and his uncle Deane had been very poor once. His uncle Glegg had saved money slowly and retired with a moderate fortune. Tom didn't want to be like his uncle Glegg; he wanted to be like his uncle Deane, who had worked his way up in a great house of business – Guest and Company – so that finally they had made him a partner.

Mr Deane was in his office, checking accounts, [1] when Tom arrived. 'Good morning, Tom. How is your father?' he asked, shaking Tom's hand.

'There has been no change,' said Tom.

'Well, what can I do for you?'

'I want to get work, Uncle.'

'How old are you now?' asked Mr Deane.

'I'm nearly seventeen.'

'Well, you've had a good education. I suppose you could do accounts. Do you understand book-keeping?' [2]

'No,' said Tom, blushing.

'What have you been learning at school, then?'

'Latin,' said Tom, 'and Greek and Roman history and Euclid and a little Algebra.'

Mr Deane lit his pipe and smoked thoughtfully, then he said,

---

1. **accounts** : detailed records of money spent and received.
2. **book-keeping** : records of the financial affairs of a business.

'Well, you've been studying these things for three years. Perhaps you should look for work where they will be useful.'

'I'd rather not, Uncle. I'm not very good at Latin and those other things, and I wouldn't want to work as a school teacher, anyway. I want to go into a business where I can work hard and get on. I want to be able to support my mother and sister.'

'Ah, young gentleman, that's not easy to do,' said Mr Deane.

'But didn't you get on in that way, Uncle?' asked Tom. 'Didn't you rise from a modest job to a more important job because of your abilities and hard work?'

'Yes, I did, and I had not been to school at all. As soon as I started work, I saw that I needed to learn accounting, to find out where the money went, and where it came from, and how much there was. So I studied in the evenings after work. I learnt all about the business and made my master's interests my own.'

'Well, Uncle,' said Tom. 'That's what I want to do.'

'Yes, but the problem is, you went to the wrong sort of school. The school you went to and the things you learned are all right for a gentleman like Mr Stephen Guest, who will have nothing to do all his life except sign cheques.'

'Don't worry, Uncle. I'll soon forget the Latin.'

'But look at your hands, Tom!' cried Mr Deane, waving his pipe in the air. 'They're soft and white. You've been trained to live like a gentleman and think like one too. You've never done a day's hard work in your life. If you want to start now, you will have to begin with a very modest job indeed. Now, if you want me to help you, I will. The best thing for you would be to work on the wharf [1] or in the warehouse, loading crates, [2] like I did. That way you could learn about the business. But you wouldn't like it, would you, Tom? You're

---

1. **wharf** [wɔːf] : structure usually made of wood beside the sea where ships may wait to have goods brought on and off.
2. **crates** : large wooden containers for transporting goods.

too fine a gentleman for that!'

'I would like to do what will be best for me in the end, even if it is difficult at first,' said Tom, with a slight tremor in his voice. 'Do you know of any job available now that I could do? I want to start work immediately.'

'If I offer you a job just because you are my nephew, I'll be responsible for you, you know,' said Mr Deane in a stern voice.

'I hope I won't do anything to disgrace you, Uncle,' Tom replied humbly.

'Well done, Tom! I won't refuse to help you, if you are determined to do well. I had better get back to work now, so good-bye.'

Mr Deane shook Tom's hand, and Tom went out into the cold damp air, feeling rather miserable.

When he got home, Maggie came to greet him and sat down with him by the fire. 'What did uncle Deane say, Tom?' she asked.

'He made me feel as if I were good for nothing. He said the things I learned at Stelling's are no use to me now. I need to know book-keeping, he said, not Latin.'

'Maybe I can find out about book-keeping,' said Maggie, 'and then I could teach you.'

'You teach me? You're always saying that kind of thing, Maggie, and it's very irritating. You always act as if you were superior to other people. For example, yesterday you should not have spoken to the aunts and uncles that way. It was stupid. You should leave it to me to take care of you and Mother. You think you know better than anyone, but you're almost always wrong. I can judge much better than you!'

Poor Tom! He had just come from his uncle Deane, who had lectured [1] him and made him feel inferior. Now he had the opportunity to treat Maggie that way, and he felt justified in doing

---

1. **lectured** : criticised.

so. Maggie was silent. She was impressed by Tom's grown-up manner, but what he said hurt her deeply. Maggie was full of passionate desires for everything that was beautiful and pleasant. She was thirsty for knowledge and full of imagination. Now the gap between what she hoped for and what she had caused her great pain. Sometimes a girl who does not seem exceptional – who will never be anything special for the world to take notice of – nevertheless feels needs and desires that will make themselves heard, often in a violent manner.

1   Choose the appropriate answer: **a**, **b**, **c** or **d**.

1   How did Tom feel when he went to see Mr Deane?
   a   ☐ confident
   b   ☐ optimistic
   c   ☐ embarrassed
   d   ☐ angry

2   Tom starts at the bottom because
   a   ☐ he had no practical experience
   b   ☐ he has studied Latin
   c   ☐ he is physically not strong
   d   ☐ he doesn't like bookkeeping

3   Why did Tom speak unkindly to Maggie? Which of these reasons would you **not** choose?
   a   ☐ because she had behaved badly the previous day
   b   ☐ because he had had a miserable day
   c   ☐ because he was feeling inferior
   d   ☐ because he had blamed his sister for their situation

2   Imagine you are Tom. Write your diary entry for the day you visited Mr Deane.

3   Chapter 11 ends with a hint. What do you think it means?

4   In chapter 12 who do you think Mrs Tulliver decides to go to see for help? Choose from the following:
   a   ☐ Mr Deane
   b   ☐ Mr Glegg
   c   ☐ Mr Wakem

5   Compare your ideas with a partner. After reading chapter 12, check if you were right.

6   Can you explain the title of chapter 12? Who is the 'hen' and who are the 'chicks'?

How a hen protects her chicks

I n the dark time of December, the household furniture was
sold. The strange man Tom and Maggie had seen in the
drawing room came every day with other men and moved all
the furniture downstairs. On the day of the sale, Tom, Maggie, and
Mrs Tulliver sat around Mr Tulliver's bed, listening to the sounds of
the people downstairs and the voice of the auctioneer. [1] They
watched Mr Tulliver anxiously, hoping he would sleep on. They did
not want him to be upset by the sounds of the sale. In his intervals of
consciousness, Mr Tulliver was becoming more irritable and bad-
tempered every day, and they knew that if he heard the auctioneer's
voice, he would get excited and start swearing about Wakem. But Mr
Tulliver did not wake up. He lay there rigid throughout the time of
the sale, in a sort of living death.

Finally it was over. The auctioneer's voice could be heard no more,
and the only sound was the tramping [2] of feet on the gravel [3] outside as
the people went away. Mrs Tulliver seemed to have aged ten years in a
single day. For the first time, Maggie noticed lines in her mother's
plump round face and streaks of white in her golden hair.

Before the sale, Mrs Tulliver had been worrying about her best
things but, when it was over, she began to think about the mill itself.
In January, signs were put up in the town, advertising the sale of the
mill and its land. Mrs Tulliver had hoped that Mr Deane might

1. **auctioneer** : person who conducts auctions.
2. **tramping** : walking with heavy steps.
3. **gravel** : small stones on a path.

persuade Guest and Company to buy the mill and keep Mr Tulliver on as manager. But Mr Deane had told her frankly that Wakem was thinking of buying the mill and would probably pay more for it than Guest and Company would be willing to pay.

Still, Mr Deane wanted to do anything he could to help the Tullivers. One day he brought Lucy to see her cousins, and on the way home she had begged him to help Maggie and Tom. So Mr Deane found Tom a temporary job in the warehouse and arranged for him to take evening lessons in book-keeping.

It was now clear that Mr Tulliver would be declared a bankrupt. The creditors would be asked to accept less money than Mr Tulliver actually owed them, and Tom found it very hard to bear that disgrace. He found his new job very difficult too. He was used to the quiet, carpeted luxury of the study room at Stelling's, but now he found himself in a big, cold, dusty warehouse, surrounded by rough, shouting men.

Mrs Tulliver, meanwhile, had a secret plan to stop Wakem from buying the mill. Imagine a respectable, good-natured hen thinking of ways to prevent the farmer from wringing [1] her neck and sending her chicks to the market. The result would probably be a lot of cackling [2] and fluttering. [3] Mrs Tulliver, seeing that everything had gone wrong, began to think that she had been too passive in life. No one else had thought of going to ask Wakem not to buy the mill, but Mrs Tulliver thought it was a good idea. Mrs Tulliver now thought that her husband had been very wrong to bring her into all this trouble, and she began to think that his opinion of Wakem might be wrong too. Perhaps Mr Wakem was not so bad after all. Perhaps he was a reasonable man. And, although he might dislike her husband, he could have nothing against Mrs Tulliver herself, an innocent and

---

1. **wringing** : twisting in order to kill.
2. **cackling** : noise hens make.
3. **fluttering** : movement of wings.

respectable lady in distress.

Mrs Tulliver kept these thoughts to herself, because she knew that Mr Deane and Mr Glegg would disapprove of the idea, and Tom disliked Wakem almost as much as his father did. So one day, without telling anybody, Mrs Tulliver went to Wakem's office, where she was shown into a private room and told to wait.

After a few minutes, Mr Wakem came into the room. He was a tall, thin man with a long, thin nose, and he seemed rather perplexed to see this plump, blonde woman waiting for him. 'Hello, Mrs Tulliver,' he said politely. 'What can I do for you?'

Now that she was sitting face to face with Mr Wakem, Mrs Tulliver began to wonder how she had found the courage to come. She felt very nervous, and at first she did not know what to say. 'I was Elizabeth Dodson, before I married, Sir. Perhaps you know my family,' she said at last.

The lawyer nodded and waited in silence.

'Well, Sir, I hope you don't think that I bear you any ill-will because my husband lost his lawsuit. The furniture has been sold, and nothing like that has ever happened in my family. I'm sure you remember my father Mr Dodson, and you know that Mrs Deane and Mrs Glegg are my sisters. We have always been a very respectable family. It's not my fault that my husband gets into lawsuits. I know he has said many bad things about you, Sir, but I never have.'

'I believe you, Mrs Tulliver,' said the lawyer with cold politeness.

'I know my husband has been very hot-tempered, but he is not a bad man, and now he lies ill at home. I told him not to go to law, but he wouldn't listen to me. And then he had a terrible attack when he heard that you had bought the mortgage on the mill. But I'm sure you will behave like a gentleman.'

'What does all this mean, Mrs Tulliver?' said Mr Wakem, rather sharply. 'What do you want to ask me?'

'Well, Sir,' said Mrs Tulliver nervously, 'I want to ask you not to buy the mill.'

'Who told you I want to buy it?'

'Mr Deane told me, Sir. And he says that Guest and Company could buy it, but that you would be willing to pay more.'

'And Guest and Company would let your husband stay on at the mill, I suppose, and pay him wages.' [1]

'Yes, Sir,' said Mrs Tulliver, 'although it makes me sad to think about my husband being paid wages. His father owned the mill before him, and his grandfather built it. But at least, if Guest and Company bought it, we could stay there in the old place.'

'What if I bought the mill and let your husband stay on as manager?'

'Oh, Sir, he would never agree to it! Your name is poison to him. He thinks of you as the cause of his ruin.'

'Then he is a fool!' cried Mr Wakem, losing his patience and rising to his feet. 'You'll have to excuse me, Mrs Tulliver. I have work to do.'

'But, Sir, please remember what I have said, and don't act against me and my children. I don't deny that my husband has been in the wrong, though he is not a bad man, and he has been punished enough. Unfortunately my children and I have been punished with him. My poor son Tom, you know, who went to school with your son, is the nicest, healthiest, handsomest boy – '

'Yes, yes. Thank you, Mrs Tulliver. I'll remember,' said Mr Wakem, leading her to the door.

'And please don't tell anyone that I came to see you, Sir, for my son would be very angry with me,' said Mrs Tulliver in a trembling voice, as she was shown out [2] into the dusty street.

When he had come into the office that morning, Mr Wakem had had no intention of buying Dorlcote Mill, but now he had changed his mind. It would be wrong to suppose that Mr Wakem hated Mr

---

1. **wages** : regular payment received for work or services.
2. **shown out** : taken to the door.

Tulliver as Mr Tulliver hated him. Mr Wakem was a very wealthy and successful man. For him, Mr Tulliver was simply a man who had lost several lawsuits from which Mr Wakem himself had gained a good income. [1] But the idea of humiliating Mr Tulliver by doing him a favour was one that appealed to [2] Mr Wakem. If Mr Wakem bought the mill but allowed Mr Tulliver to stay there as manager, society would think him very generous to his enemy, while Mr Tulliver himself would suffer the worst humiliation yet.

1. **income** : profits.
2. **appealed to** : pleased.

1 Find synonyms in chapter 12 for these adjectives. Who do they refer to?

Adjective	Synonym in chapter 12	Referent
touchy		
sensible		
reputable		

2 Are the following statements true or false? Correct those that are false.

		True	False
a	Mr Tulliver's mood had improved recently.	☐	☐
b	The auction process had had a bad effect on Mrs Tulliver.	☐	☐
c	Mrs Tulliver went to Wakem to ask him not to buy the mill.	☐	☐
d	Tom enjoyed his new job at Mr Deane's warehouse.	☐	☐
e	Mrs Tulliver felt relaxed in Mr Wakem's company.	☐	☐
f	Mrs Tulliver blames herself for her husband's position.	☐	☐

3 What do you think of Mrs Tulliver's and Wakem's behaviour? Discuss your ideas in a group of 3 students.

4 In the next chapter Mr Tulliver learns of what has happened. How do you think he will react?

Mr Tulliver comes downstairs

On a clear frosty January day, Mr Tulliver came downstairs for the first time since his accident. He did not have a clear idea of how much time had passed. Indeed, he often spoke as if he had received his lawyer's letter yesterday. Any attempt to explain to him how much time had passed was useless, because he always forgot a few hours later. His wife and children were very worried when he said he wanted to go downstairs. They feared that the shock of seeing the empty rooms would be too much for him.

The last few days had been particularly difficult, because Wakem had bought the mill and had told Mr Deane, Mr Glegg, and Mrs Tulliver that he was willing to employ Mr Tulliver as manager. This offer had caused a lot of debate in the family. The uncles and aunts thought that Mr Tulliver should accept it. They said that the only impediment was Mr Tulliver's unreasonable and childish hatred for Mr Wakem. Mr Tulliver, they said, blamed Mr Wakem for problems that were entirely his own fault. Here was an opportunity for Mr Tulliver to stay at the mill and provide for his family. Mr Tulliver himself was not present at these discussions, but Tom said he would not like to see his father employed by Wakem. Mrs Tulliver thought that her husband would never be persuaded to accept it.

'Tom,' Maggie whispered, outside their father's bedroom door, 'we must try to make Father understand a little of what has happened, before he goes downstairs.'

When Tom and Maggie went into Mr Tulliver's room, they found him dressed and sitting in the armchair. 'Ah! Maggie!' said Mr

Tulliver, 'I was just thinking about that awful letter I got yesterday.'

'It wasn't yesterday, dear Father,' said Maggie gently. 'It was nearly two months ago, and a lot of things have happened since then.' She looked at Tom in distress.

'Ah?' said her father. 'Well, anyway, if Furley cannot buy the mill, we'll find someone else to buy it. I'll take the trap and drive into St Ogg's.'

'No, Father,' said Tom. 'All that has changed. Everything is settled about the mill and the debts.'

'What has been decided, then?' asked Mr Tulliver. 'How has it been settled? They've not made me a bankrupt?'

'Oh, Father. Don't worry. We love you. Your children will always love you. And Tom has said he will pay all the rest of the money you owe the creditors when he is a man.'

Mr Tulliver began to tremble.

'I'll pay them all someday, and then you will feel better,' said Tom.

'Yes,' cried Mr Tulliver, trembling and red in the face, 'but it will be you, not me, you know. You mustn't be angry with me Tom, though you'll have a hard life. But I have given you a good education, and that should help you.'

Tom said nothing.

'Have they sold the mill, then?' asked Mr Tulliver more calmly, after a while.

'Everything is sold, but we don't know about the mill and the land yet,' said Tom. He was trying to avoid telling his father that Wakem had bought the mill.

'You must not be surprised to see the rooms looking very empty downstairs, Father,' said Maggie.

'Let's go down,' said Mr Tulliver wearily. [1]

---

1. **wearily** : tiredly.

He stood up and leaned on his stick, and Maggie took his arm.

When they were downstairs, Maggie ran ahead and moved her father's chair closer to the fire. Tom led Mr Tulliver to the chair and helped him to sit down, then he went to stand by Maggie. It was a painful moment for both Tom and Maggie, but it was worse for Tom. Tom just wanted to run away from all this sorrow. But for Maggie it was a chance to show her father how much she loved him even more clearly than before. Now he really needed her, and she would be there, at his side.

Mr Tulliver looked around the bare room at the places where familiar things had once stood. 'Ah!' he said. 'They've sold everything! Did they leave the big Bible, Tom? Everything is written in there: when I was born, when I was married...'

Tom brought the Bible to his father and opened it to the blank [1] first page, where all the dates of important family events had been written by his father and grandfather. Mrs Tulliver came in quietly and stood by the door.

Mr Tulliver pointed to a line of writing. 'My mother died when she was forty-seven,' he said. 'None of my family has lived to be very old. I too will die soon.' Then his finger moved down the page. 'It's eighteen years since I married your mother, Elizabeth Dodson. Poor Bessy!' he said, looking at her sad face, 'you were a pretty girl then – everybody said so. But you look so old and tired now. Don't be angry with me. I wanted to be a good husband to you. You said in the church when we were married that you would have me for better or worse.'

'But I never thought it would be as bad as this,' said Mrs Tulliver in a trembling voice.

'Oh Mother, don't talk that way,' said Maggie.

'Why shouldn't I talk? It's been that way all my life. Your father

---

1. **blank** : empty.

never listened to what I said, and he still won't listen now.'

'If I can do anything to please you, Bessy, I will,' said poor Mr Tulliver.

'Then say we can stay at the mill. There's no reason not to stay here, except that you hate Wakem so much.'

'Mother!' cried Tom. 'This is not the time to talk about that.'

'Let her speak,' said Mr Tulliver. 'What do you mean, Bessy?'

'I mean that Wakem has bought the mill, and he says you can stay here, which is very fair of him. He says you can be manager and have thirty shillings a week and a horse to ride.'

Mr Tulliver sank back in his chair. 'Do as you like, Bessy,' he said in a low voice. 'I've brought you to poverty. I'm nothing but a bankrupt. I can't stand up for anything anymore. This world has been too much for me. I'll work for Wakem, and we'll stay at the old mill where I was born. I'm too old and tired to change now, and I couldn't find any other work. But Tom, bring a pen and ink. I want you to write something in the Bible.'

'Oh Father! What do you want to write?' cried Maggie, pale and frightened, but her father ignored her and turned to Tom, who was back at his side with the pen and ink.

'Now, Tom, write that your father, Edward Tulliver, agreed to work for Wakem, the man who had ruined him. Put that in the right words, Tom. Then write that even so, I do not forgive Wakem. And, though I will work hard for him, I wish that evil may befall him! [1] Write that.'

'Oh no, Father! Don't make him write that!' cried Maggie.

There was a dead silence while Tom wrote the words. Mrs Tulliver looked frightened, and Maggie trembled like a leaf.

'Have you finished? Very well. Now write that you will remember what Wakem has done to your father, and when you are older you

---

1. **evil may befall him** : evil things will happen to him.

will punish him for it. And then sign your name: Thomas Tulliver.'

'I beg you, Father, don't make Tom write that!' cried Maggie.

'Be quiet, Maggie,' said Tom. 'I *shall* write it!'

1 Here are the answers to some questions based on chapter 13. Can you write the questions?

  a Because Mr Tulliver wanted to go downstairs and they were scared that he would be shocked by the empty rooms.

  b He was prepared to offer Mr Tulliver a job at the mill.

  c Tom promises to pay his father's creditors.

  d He makes him vow in writing in the Bible that he will punish Wakem.

2 In this chapter, Mr Tulliver is eventually defeated by events. When does this happen? Did you expect this reaction?

3 Imagine you are Tom. What are your thoughts when you hear your father say 'But I have given you a good education, and that should help you'?

4 The chapter provides further evidence of Tom and Maggie's contrasting personalities in their reaction to events. Find one example for both Tom and Maggie.

5 In the next chapter Maggie finds help in the form of a 'voice from the past'. Who or what do you think this 'voice' could be? Choose one of the three possibilities below. Go back and check after you have read chapter 14.

  a A friend from her childhood.

  b A relative she hasn't seen for a long time.

  c An old book.

A voice from the past

As Mr Tulliver gradually got stronger, his old pride and defiance [1] got stronger too. He was withdrawn [2] and bad-tempered. He went back to work and received his wages from Wakem. He saved as much money as he could and kept it in an old tin box. Tom too was working hard and saving; he too put his savings in the tin box. The only thing that brought a smile to Mr Tulliver's face was the sight of the money they had saved. Although he still loved Maggie very much and needed her by his side, he no longer showed his affection as he had before. When she sat beside her father in the evenings, she wished that he would stroke her hair as he used to do, but he never did. And Tom was tired and gloomy when he came home in the evenings. He never showed signs of affection for Maggie – never called her 'Magsie' anymore. He did not even speak to her very much. Maggie felt sad and lonely.

Now that her father and Tom were so cold and distant, she felt the need of love. There seemed to be no love in her life now. She often felt angry with Tom and her parents for being so different from what she wanted them to be. The strength of her anger frightened her. It was like the eruption of a volcano and made her think that there were demons in her soul. Her empty life was even harder to bear because she wanted so much – more, it seemed, than other people wanted. She wished she could be like Tom and bury herself in some useful work.

Sometimes she thought she could be content if she had books to read, so that she could live through her imagination, but most of her

---

1. **defiance** : confrontation.
2. **withdrawn** : distant.

books had been sold with the furniture. One day, Bob Jakin came to visit. Bob was now a grown man of twenty. He had got married and lived with his wife and mother in the old, round house by the river. Bob made a living buying and selling things. He went everywhere with a pack on his back, and in the pack he had all sorts of things for sale.

'Good morning, Miss,' said Bob.

'Oh, Bob! How good to see you!' said Maggie with a smile.

'I just dropped by to give you these, Miss,' said Bob. He opened his pack and took out some books. 'I remember how much you like reading, and I know you lost all your books in the sale, so when I saw these, I thought perhaps you would like them.'

'How very kind of you, Bob,' said Maggie. The books were old and worn, and they were not the sort of books that Maggie usually read, but she felt very grateful for Bob's kindness.

A few days later, Maggie looked through the books that Bob had brought her. Among them she found *Imitation of Christ* by Thomas à Kempis. [1] Religion had never interested Maggie as much as poetry, but now that her books of Scott [2] and Byron [3] were gone, she took up this little, battered book by Thomas à Kempis with curiosity.

The corners of some pages had been folded down, and someone had marked certain passages with a pen: 'Know that your love of yourself hurts you more than anything in the world... If you want things or want to be somewhere else, you will never be content, because you will always find what you have disappointing... Wherever you go you will find suffering. The only way to find inner peace is to be patient: stop thinking about yourself and desiring things you do not have... You suffer little compared to the sufferings

---

1. **Thomas à Kempis** : (*c*. 1380-1471) a medieval monk and devotional writer, born near Cologne.
2. **Scott** : Sir Walter Scott (1771-1832) Scottish poet and novelist.
3. **Byron** : Lord George Gordon Byron (1788-1824) poet.

of the saints. Think of their suffering, and you will be able to bear your own.'

These words had a profound effect on Maggie. She felt as if her soul had been sleeping. Here was a secret that would enable her to improve her life without the help of other people or things. She suddenly realised that her misery came from wanting too much. If she could look at her own life as an insignificant part of God's plan, instead of thinking of herself as the centre of the universe, she could be content. That day she read the whole book eagerly.

The next day she began to plan what she would do to begin her new life. She would work hard at plain sewing, making simple garments that could be sold at the market, so that she too could add something to the old tin box. She would read nothing but the Bible and Thomas à Kempis. She would never look in the mirror and, to help her in this resolution, she removed the mirror from her bedroom wall.

For two years, this way of living helped Maggie to find contentment. Her mother noticed the change, and often watched Maggie as she sat sewing in the drawing room. Maggie was growing tall and handsome, and now that Mrs Tulliver had no 'best things' to be proud of, she began to be proud of Maggie. She was even proud of Maggie's thick dark hair, which had once been so much trouble to her, and she spent hours brushing and arranging it.

'Look, Mr Tulliver!' said Mrs Tulliver to her husband more than once. 'What lovely hair it is now!'

But Mr Tulliver did not look and replied brusquely, 'I always knew she would be a handsome woman. It is a pity she'll be wasted. Since she has no money, no one who's fit [1] for her will want to marry her.'

---

1. **fit** : (here) right, good enough.

1 Time passes and Maggie, Tom and their father have changed. Put these adjectives into their comparative form. Who do you associate them with? You will probably use some adjectives for more than one character.

Adjective	Comparative form	Character
sad		
proud		
strong		
lonely		
defiant		
affectionate	(negative comparative)	

2 What are the psychological and physical effects of *Imitation of Christ* on Maggie? Do you think her new-found serenity can last?

3 Mr Tulliver has always been pessimistic about his daughter's prospects! Why? (Go back also to chapter 1)

PART 2

1 In the table below there should be 10 sentences which summarise the main events in part 2 (chapters 9 to 14). However, 3 sentences are missing. Complete the table with the event and the chapter number.

Chapter	Event number	Event
9	1	Mr Furley has sold the mortgage on the mill to Wakem.
10	2	The Dodsons decide to buy only some of the Tullivers' furniture.
	3	
12	4	The Tullivers' furniture is auctioned.
12	5	Mrs Tulliver goes to speak to Wakem.
	6	
13	7	Mr Tulliver accepts the inevitability of working for Wakem.
13	8	Mr Tulliver makes Tom vow to take revenge on Wakem.
	9	
14	10	Maggie is profoundly affected by the *Imitation of Christ*.

2 Now write a short summary of the main events in part 2 as you did for part 1, using between 120 and 180 words.

3 'The image of Maggie is of a volcano, full of angry force waiting to be unleashed.'
   Go back and find all the episodes in parts 1 and 2 when Maggie explodes. There are five in total. Make a note of the recurring vocabulary used to describe these events. Events number 1 and 2 have been done for you.

Event	Page	Key phrase
1	23	She felt as if small demons had taken possession of her soul.
2	24	Suddenly all the pain and anger...
3		
4		
5		

4 **Law, lawyers and bankruptcy in the early Victorian novel**
   The fear of bankruptcy and its consequences, and the presentation of the lawyer as a cruel and heartless figure are both recurring themes in the English novel of the period, particularly in the work of Charles Dickens. In fact, Wakem has been described as Eliot's most Dickensian creation. Find out the reasons for Dickens' aversion to the law and some of his most famous fictional creations. This could be done in the form of a class project in which the class is divided into groups with specific information to find out.

5 In chapter 9 Mrs Tulliver is extremely upset at losing her possessions. Have you got a special possession which you would hate to lose? Write a brief description of it, saying why it is important to you.

6 In chapter 10 Mrs Deane and Mr and Mrs Glegg are deciding what to do after the bankruptcy of Mr Tulliver. Imagine you are a young relative of the Deane or Glegg family. You are now a grandparent but you still vividly remember the scene. Write a short account of the scene as if you were telling it to your grandchild.

MAGGIE AND PHILIP

CHAPTER ◆ 15

In the Red Deeps

One day in June, when Maggie was seventeen years old, Mr Wakem came to the mill to check the accounts. Maggie was sitting by the window sewing, and she saw him arrive on horseback. He was not alone. Philip was riding beside him on a handsome pony. Seeing her at the window, Philip raised his hat to Maggie, and Mr Wakem looked at both of them sharply. Maggie hurried away from the window and took her sewing upstairs. She did not want to meet Philip again after all these years, in the presence of their two fathers.

A few days later, Maggie went for a walk in the woods near Dorlcote Mill. These woods, which were known as the Red Deeps, had frightened Maggie when she was a child. She had imagined them full of thieves and wild animals. But now they were full of wild roses, and Maggie loved to walk there alone.

As she was enjoying the fresh air and looking up at the fir trees, she heard a sound behind her and turned to see Philip Wakem walking towards her. Philip blushed and raised his hat. Maggie blushed a little too, as she looked down at his poor deformed figure, remembering their childhood times together.

'Hello,' she said. 'I've never met anyone in these woods before. What are you doing here? Did you come to find me?'

'Yes. I saw you leave the house, and so I followed you here. I hope you don't mind.'

'No, I'm glad you came,' said Maggie. 'I have never forgotten our talks at Stelling's school. Tom and I have had a lot of trouble since then.'

'I have thought of you a lot over the years,' said Philip. 'I even did a painting of you.' He showed Maggie a small, water-colour portrait of herself as she had looked then.

'Oh dear!' said Maggie, smiling and blushing with pleasure. 'What a funny girl I was. I really did look like a gypsy. I suppose I still do. Do I look as you imagined I would?'

'No,' said Philip. 'You are far more beautiful than I imagined.'

'Am I?' said Maggie, turning away from him to hide her blush. They walked in silence for a while, then Maggie said, 'I wish we could still be friends, but it wouldn't be right now. It is the same with everything. I have lost everything I used to love when I was little. The books are gone, and Tom is different, and so is my father. It is like death. We cannot be friends now, Philip. My father would never allow it.'

'I understand,' said Philip, 'but it is wrong to sacrifice everything because of other people's unreasonable feelings. I would do almost anything for my father, but I would not give up a friendship just because he told me to do so.'

'Sometimes I feel that way too,' said Maggie, 'but I'm sure that it is wrong. I would rather sacrifice anything than make my father's life even harder than it is.'

'But will it make his life harder if we meet sometimes?'

'He wouldn't like it,' Maggie replied. 'My father feels so strongly about some things. He is not at all happy.'

'Neither am I!' said Philip impetuously.

'Why? Why aren't you happy, Philip?' asked Maggie, but Philip walked on without answering. After a while, Maggie spoke again: 'I've been much happier since I have stopped thinking about my own wants. Wishing for things we cannot have only makes us miserable.'

'But I can't give up wishing,' said Philip impatiently. 'No one who is really alive can give up wishing and longing for [1] things. There are certain things we feel are beautiful and good. How can we ever be satisfied without them? I love fine paintings, and I try so hard to paint well, but I never produce what I want. And there are many other things I long for,' – here Philip hesitated a little – 'things that other men have but I can never have.'

'Oh, Philip, I wish you didn't feel that way,' said Maggie, but in her heart she knew she felt that way too.

'I would be happy if I could see you sometimes,' said Philip. 'I have no friends, no one to whom I can tell everything. If you would let me meet you here just once or twice a month, I would be content.'

Maggie was silent and thoughtful. It seemed as if two voices were arguing in her mind. One voice said yes: such meetings would be not only innocent but good. Perhaps she could help Philip to find contentment as she had found it. But the other voice said no: the meetings would be secret, she would be deceiving her father, and if her father ever found out he would be angry and hurt. Then the first voice spoke again and said that it was not fair to reject Philip because of her father's unreasonable wish, when Philip had to suffer so much rejection because of his deformity. The idea that he might become her lover, or that other people might think that, never occurred to her. [2]

'I can't decide now,' said Maggie. 'I must think about it. I don't want to make a mistake.'

'Then I will come here as often as I can, Maggie, and hope to see you here, and you can tell me what you have decided.'

'All right,' said Maggie. 'I must go now. Good-bye Philip.'

Philip watched her as she hurried away between the slanting [3] shadows of the great fir trees.

---

1. **longing for** : desiring.
2. **never occurred to her** : she never thought of it.
3. **slanting** : inclining.

1 After two years of comparative contentment Maggie's meeting with Philip awakes old desires and needs. Maggie has 'two voices...arguing in her mind' (page 77). One voice is of self-sacrifice and responsibility to her father, as influenced by the *Imitation of Christ* (pages 70-1); the other voice desires love and beauty. Find examples of the conflicting voices in the chapter and identify the speaker. An example has been done for you.

The voice of self-sacrifice	The voice of desire for love and beauty
• I wish we could still be friends, but it wouldn't be right now (Maggie)	• It is wrong to sacrifice everything because of other people's unreasonable feelings (Philip)
•	•
•	•
•	•
•	

2 Which 'voice' does Philip have?

3 What does Maggie decide at the end of the chapter?

4 **Places**

a How do you imagine the Red Deeps? Work individually and write at least three sentences describing the wood. Think of colour, light, types of trees, etc. You will obviously need to use a dictionary! When you have finished, compare your sentences with a partner's.

b Do you have a favourite place? Prepare the vocabulary you will need to describe it. Try and build up lexical chains as in the diagram below. Use an English learner's dictionary for help.

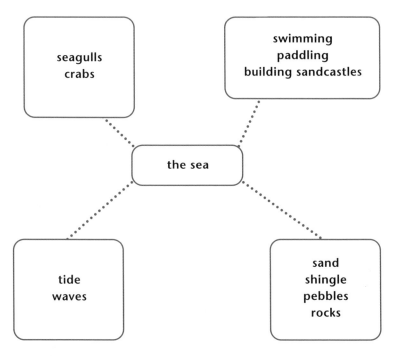

c In small groups describe the place and say why it is important for you. Be prepared to ask and answer questions for more information. In the extension exercises for part 3 you will be asked to write your description.

 5 Go back and listen to Philip and Maggie's dialogue on pages 75-77. Do you think they sound completely at ease with each other or are they slightly embarrassed?

CHAPTER 16

Tom's business venture

Tom worked hard for Guest and Company, and his uncle Deane watched him closely. Soon Mr Deane began to feel rather proud of this nephew he had brought into the business. When Tom had learned all he could in the warehouse, Mr Deane began to send him on short trips to buy raw materials for the company. This job involved more responsibility than working in the warehouse. In the second year, Tom's salary was raised, and everything except the price of his food and clothes went into the tin box. He wanted to succeed in life, and the first step was to pay his father's debts and thus restore his family's good name. As Tom became wiser in business, he began to understand just how imprudent his father had been.

Soon the aunts and uncles realised that Tom was very different from his father. They were pleased to see that he took after the Dodson side of the family. For a while they considered giving him some financial help, but then they decided against it: the boy was doing very well on his own. Tom, meanwhile, expected no help from anyone. He noticed that other young men who worked for Guest and Company were making extra money by doing a little trading of their own. They would spend their savings on a small cargo [1] of woollen cloth, for example, and sell it to a merchant in a foreign country. Tom was delighted with the idea. Saving money had been such a very slow process. Here was an opportunity to make a profit quickly. But first he had to persuade his father to let him have some money out of the tin box.

---

1. **cargo** : amount of goods, load.

Tom sat by the fire with his father one evening and explained the plan to him carefully. Mr Tulliver listened with a doubtful expression on his face. He wanted to say no, but he realised that Tom was doing well and that perhaps his own judgement in matters of business was not as good as Tom's. So finally he took the tin box out and counted the money. After two years of hard work and saving, there were still only one hundred and sixteen pounds in the box.

'How much do you want?' asked Mr Tulliver.

'Could I have thirty-six pounds, Father?'

Mr Tulliver counted out thirty-six pounds. 'It took me a year to save that,' he said in a resentful voice.

'Yes, I know, but this way we might double our savings,' said Tom.

Mr Tulliver kept his hand over the money. 'But you might lose it, Tom!' he said.

'I won't take it, if you don't want me to, Father,' said Tom. And he watched as Mr Tulliver put the thirty-six pounds with the rest back in the tin box.

Tom decided to ask his uncle Glegg to invest twenty pounds and to pay him five percent of the profit. The next day he went to Mr Glegg's house and found him in the garden. When Tom had explained everything, Mr Glegg nodded his head in approval and said, 'It sounds like a good plan, Tom. Why don't you invest some of your savings in it?'

'I did ask Father, Sir, but he was worried about losing the money.'

'Well, I might lend you thirty pounds to invest, Tom.'

'Mr Glegg!' called his wife from the window. 'Come and have your tea. Oh! Hello, Tom. I didn't know you were here.'

'We're coming, my dear,' said Mr Glegg, and he and Tom went into the house. 'Tom here was just telling me about a business venture of his,' said Mr Glegg, taking a cup of tea.

'What business venture?' asked Mrs Glegg with a frown.

When Tom had explained the whole thing again, Mrs Glegg said, 'Well, I hope it's not my money you are thinking of giving him, Mr Glegg!'

'It's not giving him money, Jane: it's an investment. Instead of keeping your money in an old sock under the bed, you could invest it and make some more.'

'And the interest, Aunt, is twelve percent,' said Tom.

'Twelve percent!' cried Mrs Glegg. 'Why did no one tell me about this before? Mr Glegg said that I could not get more than five percent on my savings!'

'That's true,' said Mr Glegg. 'You can't get more than five percent with security. If you want twelve percent, you have to risk your savings in trade.'

'But the risk is not very great, Aunt,' said Tom.

'Well,' said Mrs Glegg. 'You seem to be a sensible boy. Perhaps we will lend you the money after all.'

Tom invested the money his aunt and uncle had lent him, and all went well. He paid them back the thirty pounds and invested his profits again. He did not tell his father about it, partly because he did not want his father to interfere and partly because he wanted to surprise him when he had accumulated enough money to pay off the debts. By the time of Maggie's first meeting with Philip in the Red Deeps, Tom had a hundred and fifty pounds of his own capital. He was twenty-one years old, and the life ahead of him was beginning to look brighter.

1 What is the significance of the following numbers?

   a 116   **b** 36   **c** 30   **d** 12   **e** 150

2 How do Tom and Maggie's prospects compare? Chapter 16 ends
   optimistically for Tom: '…life ahead of him was beginning to look
   brighter'. What possible problems could upset these prospects? Make
   some predictions and compare them with your partner. Keep a record
   of them as you go on in the story.

3 The title of the next chapter is 'The wavering balance'; this means
   something is undecided or in doubt. Who do you think has the doubts
   and what about? Choose the most likely answer.

   a Maggie is unsure about continuing to read novels.

   b Maggie is unsure about meeting Philip.

   c Philip is unsure about meeting Maggie.

   d Tom is unsure about his sister's behaviour.

CHAPTER 17

The wavering [1] balance

The two voices in Maggie's mind argued all week. Then she went for a walk in the Red Deeps, hoping to see Philip and tell him that they could not meet again. She had looked forward to seeing him all day. It was so wonderful to talk to someone who admired her and was interested in what she said. Nevertheless, she had made up her mind.

'I'm sorry, Philip,' she said, when they met among the tall fir trees. 'I cannot meet you here in secret. It would be wrong.'

Philip looked upset. 'Well, Maggie,' he said. 'If we must part, let's try to forget it for a little while. Let's walk together for the last time.'

He took her hand, and they walked on in silence. Then Philip said, 'I am going to paint another portrait of you. It will be a large oil painting of you as a Hamadryad, [2] coming out of one of these great fir trees in the evening light.'

'Do you like painting more than anything else now, Philip?' asked Maggie.

'No. I love painting, but I also love singing and reading. Look, I have just finished reading this book. I enjoyed it very much. Perhaps you would like to have it.'

Philip showed her a copy of *The Pirate* by Sir Walter Scott. For a moment, Maggie felt full of joy at the idea of reading it. Then she remembered that she had given up reading novels.

'Thank you, but I can't take it,' she said.

'Why not?'

'I don't read that sort of book anymore. I find those books make me

1. **wavering** : unstable.
2. **Hamadryad** : in Greek mythology, hamadryads were nymphs who inhabited trees.

long for things I cannot have.'

'Oh, Maggie!' cried Philip impatiently. 'This is ridiculous. You can't deny yourself everything. If you do, your emotions will one day burst out, like a savage appetite. What harm is there in enjoying the few pleasures that are available to you?'

Maggie's eyes filled with tears. 'Why are you trying to tempt me?' she cried.

Philip felt sorry for having spoken so harshly. 'Let's not talk about it any more, Maggie. We only have a little time together.'

'What a dear, good brother you would have been, Philip,' said Maggie. 'If you had been my brother, I think you would have loved me well enough to forgive me anything. I always wished that Tom would love me like that. I was never satisfied with a little of anything. Oh Philip, I must go home now.'

'Maggie, please change your mind. Don't say we can never meet again. If I come and walk here sometimes, and we meet by accident, you will be doing nothing wrong.'

Maggie looked at him with startled eyes, but she did not forbid him to come to the Red Deeps. She merely said good-bye and went home.

1 'The two voices in Maggie's mind argued all week.'
   At the end of chapter 16 you were asked to predict what the wavering
   balance was. In chapter 17 we see that it concerned Maggie's conflict
   about seeing Philip or not. Make a list of the arguments in favour of
   both 'voices' present throughout the chapter. There are more in favour
   than against.

Arguments in favour of meeting Philip	Arguments against meeting Philip
• • • •	• • •

2 Imagine you are a friend of Maggie's and have received this letter
   below. Advise Maggie to follow one of the 'voices'. Write a short reply
   using only the ideas which you collected in exercise 1. You will be asked
   to express your own ideas at the end of part 3. In chapter 3, exercise 5
   we saw that a function (doing or performing something with words)
   can be expressed in different ways. In this letter you are advising. Before
   you write, check with a partner the various advice structures you know
   and those you will use *(If I were you I'd..., I think you should...,
   I would...).*

   ... thinking about this problem all week. My dearest friend, how I would
   appreciate your guidance!
   Write to me and help me resolve this turmoil I am suffering.

   Your trusted friend,
   Maggie

3 The next chapter is entitled 'Another love scene'. Which 'voice' has, for
   the time being, won?

CHAPTER 18

Another love scene

E arly the following April, nearly a year later, Maggie was in the Red Deeps again, waiting for Philip. They had met there many times over the last year, and Philip had brought books for Maggie. When Philip arrived, Maggie gave him back his copy of *Corinne* by Madame de Staël. 'Take it back,' she said, laughing. 'I didn't finish it. As soon as I got to the part where the blonde young lady is reading in the park, I shut the book and decided to read no more of it. I foresaw that the blonde young lady would win all the love, and poor dark-haired Corinne would be miserable. I won't read any more books in which the blonde women get all the happiness. Give me a story in which a dark-haired woman triumphs for a change.'

'Maybe you will avenge the dark-haired women yourself and carry all the love away from your cousin Lucy. There is sure to be some handsome young man of St Ogg's in love with Lucy at the moment. All you have to do is smile at him, and Lucy will be quite forgotten.'

'Don't say that, Philip,' cried Maggie, looking hurt. 'I would never do anything to hurt Lucy and, besides, she is ten times prettier than I am.'

'I was only joking, Maggie,' said Philip with surprise.

'Anyway,' said Maggie. 'It is not because I am dark myself that I want the dark women to win; it is because I always feel sorry for the rejected lover in the story. If the blonde woman were rejected, I'd feel sorry for her too.'

'Then you would never be able to reject a lover yourself, would you, Maggie?' said Philip, blushing a little.

'I don't know,' said Maggie. 'Maybe I would, if he were conceited. ¹ But if he were very unhappy afterwards, I would relent.' ²

'I have often wondered,' said Philip, with some effort, 'whether you would be more likely to love a man that other women were not likely to love.'

'That would depend. The other women might dislike him because he was unpleasant or conceited.'

'But suppose,' said Philip, 'he was not conceited. Suppose he felt he had nothing to be conceited about. Suppose it was someone who had been marked from childhood for a peculiar kind of suffering – and he loved you very much...'

Philip fell silent, frightened that his words had offended her. Maggie walked towards the trunk of a fallen tree and sat down on it, as if all the strength had suddenly gone out of her legs. 'I am so surprised, Philip. I never imagined...'

'I was a fool to say it, Maggie. Please forgive me. Has it made you hate me?'

'How can you think that? I am grateful for any love. But... but I had never thought of you being my lover.'

'Then can you bear to think of me as your lover, Maggie?' asked Philip, sitting down beside her, suddenly full of hope. 'Do you love me?'

Maggie turned rather pale: this direct question was not easy to answer. 'I don't think I could love anyone better,' she said. 'But let's not say any more about it. We couldn't even be friends, if our friendship were discovered. I have never felt right about meeting you here, although I have loved our conversations, and now I am afraid again that it will lead to evil.'

'But if you had been guided by that fear before, you would have

1. **conceited** : arrogant.
2. **relent** : soften.

lived through another year of loneliness and self-denial, [1] instead of reading and laughing and talking to me.'

'It has been very sweet, I know – all our talks together and the books and the feeling that I had our walk in the woods to look forward to. But it has made me restless: I have impatient thoughts and am unsatisfied with my home. I think it was better when I had no selfish desires.'

'Don't think of the past now, Maggie. Think only of our love. If you really love me, all the obstacles will be overcome in time. Tell me again: is it possible for you to love me? Don't look away.'

She turned her dark eyes on him with a sad smile. 'Come on, Maggie. Say one kind word, or else I'll say that you were better to me at Stelling's school. Remember, you promised to kiss me when we met again, but you never kept your promise.'

Remembering that childish time was a relief to Maggie. It made the present moment seem less strange. She kissed him as he had done when she was twelve years old. Philip's eyes were full of delight, but his next words were words of discontent: 'You don't seem happy enough, Maggie. You are forcing yourself to say you love me out of pity.'

'No, I'm not, Philip. It's all so new and strange to me, but I don't think I could love anyone better than I love you. I would like to make you happy. There is only one thing I will not do for your sake: I will not hurt my father. You must never ask me to do that. But what would your own father say, Philip? Oh, it is quite impossible for us to be anything more than friends – brother and sister in secret – as we have been. Let's forget trying to be anything else.'

'No, Maggie, I can't give you up, unless you are deceiving me and really only love me as a brother. Tell me the truth.'

'Indeed I do, Philip. I have never been so happy as I am when

---

1. **self-denial** : renunciation.

I'm with you, except when I was little when Tom was good to me. I shall never be tired of being with you.'

'Then my life will be filled with hope, Maggie, and I will be happier than other men, in spite of everything.'

She had a moment of real happiness then: for a moment she believed that, if there were any sacrifice in this love, it made it richer and more satisfying.

A C T I V I T I E S

1 Choose the appropriate phrase or sentence **a**, **b**, **c** or **d**.

1 Maggie stopped reading *Corinne* because
- **a** ☐ she wanted the dark-haired woman to win
- **b** ☐ she found the story predictable
- **c** ☐ she does not like blonde-haired women in stories

2 Maggie would also feel sorry for a blonde-haired woman if
- **a** ☐ she were rejected
- **b** ☐ her lover was unpleasant or conceited
- **c** ☐ she was very unhappy

3 Philip tells Maggie of his love for her
- **a** ☐ openly
- **b** ☐ indirectly
- **c** ☐ jokingly

4 Which of the following statements is not true? Maggie
- **a** ☐ would like to be loved by Philip
- **b** ☐ is prepared to hurt her father to defend their relationship
- **c** ☐ loves Philip like a brother

2 When Philip asks Maggie if she loves him she '...turned rather pale: this direct question was not easy to answer.' (page 88). Why is Maggie not at ease about her relationship with Philip?
Answer the question remembering the following points:

   a Family loyalty.

   b Voice influenced by *Imitation of Christ*.

   c Maggie's compassion for the 'rejected'.

3 There is a hint about a future event in the story. Can you find it?

4 In the next chapter, Tom discovers the truth. How do you think he will find out? Discuss with a partner which of the following you think are possible or unlikely. Give reasons for your answers.

   a Mrs Glegg has seen Maggie and Philip together in the Red Deeps.

   b Tom is suspicious when Maggie becomes embarrassed at the mention of Philip.

   c Philip has told people in St Ogg's of his relationship with Maggie.

   d Tom is suspicious of Maggie's dirty shoes.

   e Wakem, who has found out about Philip's relationship with Maggie by reading his diary, tells Tom.

CHAPTER 19

Tom discovers the truth

For the whole year that Maggie had been meeting Philip in the Red Deeps, she had been afraid of her father or Tom coming across them by accident. But in fact their secret meetings were discovered in a completely different way. It was one Sunday, when Mr and Mrs Glegg had come to lunch.

'You look very well, Maggie!' said Mrs Glegg. 'I never thought, Bessy, that your daughter would grow up to be so good-looking.'

'It's a pity she can't have nice clothes, like her cousin Lucy,' said Mrs Tulliver. 'Nice clothes make all the difference in a girl's beauty.'

'They say that Lucy is the prettiest girl in St Ogg's,' said Mr Glegg. 'And Deane is doing so well that he can buy her all the nice clothes she wants.'

'She might be pretty,' said Mr Tulliver, 'but she's too small. I don't admire small women. They look silly by the side of men. When I chose my wife, I chose her just the right size: neither too little nor too big.'

Poor Mrs Tulliver, who now looked very old and worn, smiled complacently.

'Big or little is not the important thing,' said Mrs Glegg. 'The important thing is that they are healthy and well made. Not like Wakem's son, poor boy. It's painful to look at him.'

'And when do you have to look at him, Mrs Glegg?' said her husband, smiling and winking [1] at the others.

'I see him often enough,' said Mrs Glegg, 'coming out of the Red

---

1. **winking** : signalling by opening and shutting an eye.

Deeps just across the road from our house. Goodness knows what
he's doing there. They say he's an unfriendly, solitary kind of boy. I
suppose he goes there to walk on his own in the woods.'

Maggie blushed red and felt her hands trembling. Tom was
sitting opposite her at the table. When she looked up at him, he
looked away. Maggie was sure that Tom had seen her agitation, but
she hoped that he would think that she was just worried that the
mention of Wakem's name would upset her father.

Tom, however, had seen clearly that the cause of Maggie's
distress was something deeper. He remembered hearing his mother
complain that Maggie was always dirtying her boots on her walks in
the Red Deeps, and he began to suspect. But he could not believe
that Maggie was in love with Philip. He had always felt repulsion
for Philip's deformity, and he could not imagine any woman falling
in love with him. Even if it were only friendship, it must be stopped
immediately. She was disobeying her father and her brother, and
she was risking her reputation by meeting Philip in secret.

The next day, at the warehouse, Tom saw Philip walking on the
other side of the river, going towards the Red Deeps. He told the
manager that he had to leave on urgent family business, and set off
home by the quickest way. Just as he got to the house, he saw
Maggie coming out of the door.

'Tom! Why have you come home?' she asked in a tremulous
voice.

'I've come to walk with you in the Red Deeps and meet Philip
Wakem.'

Maggie stood helpless, pale and cold. At last, she said, 'I'm not
going.'

'Yes, you are,' said Tom, and he took her arm and started
walking rapidly down the path. 'How long have you been meeting
Philip Wakem?'

'A year.'

'And what has happened between you?'

'We have been friends. He lent me books.'

'Is that all?' demanded Tom.

'No,' said Maggie. 'On Saturday he told me that he loved me – I didn't think of it before then – I had only thought of him as an old friend.'

'And what did you say?' asked Tom, with an expression of disgust.

'I told him that I loved him too.'

Tom was silent for a few moments, looking at the ground and frowning, with his hands in his pockets. At last he looked up and said coldly, 'Now Maggie, there are two things you can do: either you swear to me that you will never see Philip Wakem again, or you refuse, and I tell Father everything. I have been working hard and saving money to pay Father's debts, so that our family can be respected again, and all the time you have been doing things that will drive Father mad with anger! Now I have the money to pay the debts, and I hoped our father would be happy again before he dies. You have to choose, Maggie! Choose!'

'Do you really have the money to pay the debts?' cried Maggie, feeling a moment of joy in the midst of all her sorrow.

'Yes!'

'I was wrong to do it, Tom,' said Maggie, 'but I was so lonely, and Philip was unhappy. I promise not to see him again.'

They walked along quickly and in silence. Maggie was thinking of all the pain Philip would feel, and she was afraid of the harsh words Tom would say to him. They entered the Red Deeps and passed among the great fir trees. In the distance they saw Philip, sitting on the fallen tree. Philip saw them coming and stood up. For a horrible moment, Maggie imagined her tall, strong brother grasping the feeble Philip, crushing him and trampling [1] on him.

---

1. **trampling** : walking heavily and violently.

'What do you mean, Sir,' began Tom in an angry voice, 'by taking advantage of a young girl's foolishness?'

'I didn't take advantage!' cried Philip. 'I would never do anything that would make your sister unhappy. I love her more than you do!'

'Do you mean to say that you didn't know that meeting you here could ruin her reputation?' asked Tom scornfully. 'You had no right to tell her you loved her, even if you had been a fit husband for her, because neither your father nor hers would ever agree to a marriage between you! How dare you – you! – worm your way into [1] the affections of a handsome girl not yet eighteen years old, who has been shut out of the world by her father's misfortunes!'

'You are incapable of understanding what I feel for your sister,' said Philip bitterly. 'I feel so much for her that I even want to be friends with you.'

'I don't want to understand your feelings,' said Tom. 'I want you to understand that I shall take care of my sister, and if you come near her again your miserable deformed body will not protect you. I shall thrash [2] you, Sir, and everyone will laugh at you! Who would not laugh at the idea of you as the lover of a fine girl?'

'Tom, stop!' cried Maggie.

'Wait, Maggie!' said Philip, then he turned to Tom. 'I suppose you have dragged your sister here so that she can watch you threaten and insult me. But let her speak. If she says we must part, I will obey her.'

'It is for my father's sake, Philip,' cried Maggie. 'Tom says he will tell my father, and he couldn't bear it! I have promised Tom that I will never see you again.'

'All right,' said Philip. 'My feelings won't change. I want you to know that. But consider yourself entirely free. I only want what is good for you.'

---

1. **worm your way into** : try to win in a dishonest way.
2. **thrash** : hit.

Tom grasped Maggie's arm and hurried away. When they were out of the woods, Maggie pulled herself away from Tom and stopped. 'Don't suppose that I think you are right, Tom,' she said bitterly. 'I hate the way you spoke to Philip. How dare you say those things about his deformity! You have criticised other people all your life. You have always been sure that you yourself were right. It is because your mind is not large enough to see anything better than your own petty aims!' [1]

'I don't think you have acted better than I have,' said Tom coldly. 'I know what my aims were, and I have succeeded in them! What were your aims? And what good have they brought to you or anyone else?'

'I know I have often been wrong, Tom, but sometimes, when I have been wrong, it was because I have feelings that you have never had! If you had done anything wrong, I would be sorry for the pain it caused you. I wouldn't enjoy seeing you punished!'

'If your feelings are so fine,' said Tom sarcastically, 'why not show them in a way that will not bring disgrace on the family? I have shown my feelings in a very different way, by working to pay off Father's debts!'

'Because you are a man and have power and can do something to change the world!'

'Well, if you can do nothing, you should obey those who can!' said Tom.

'I will obey what I feel to be right. I will even obey what I feel to be wrong, if the order comes from my father, but not from you, Tom. I will not give up Philip Wakem in obedience to you. Your insults to his deformity make me want to take care of him even more!'

'All right, Maggie. I see now how much we disagree. Let's remember that in future and be silent,' said Tom, more coldly than

---

1. **petty aims** : insignificant aspirations.

ever. He went back to St Ogg's and his work.

Maggie went to her room and wept. Then she started to think of the quiet time before she had first met Philip in the Red Deeps. If she had thought that she was entirely wrong and that Tom was entirely right, it would have been easier for her. It pained her to think of Philip, and of the insulting things that Tom had said to him. And yet, she felt a kind of relief as well. Why was that? she wondered. Surely it was only because she had no secrets from her family now?

A C T I V I T I E S

1 In chapter 18, exercise 4 you were asked to consider some possible ways in which Tom finds out about Maggie's relationship with Philip. Were you right?

2 This is a long chapter which can be divided into 4 sections. Choose the most appropriate title for each section (there is one extra you will not need!) and decide where each section ends.

 a Maggie's anger and relief.

 b Tom becomes suspicious.

 c Philip defends his family.

 d Tom and Philip clash.

 e Maggie tells Tom the truth.

Section 1	Section 2	Section 3	Section 4
Ends:	Ends:	Ends:	Ends:

Section 1

1 What vocabulary transmits Maggie's sense of fear?

2 Three clues reveal Maggie's secret. What are they?

3 Do you think Tom is justified in wanting Maggie's relationship with Philip to end?

Section 2

1 Explain Tom's reaction of disgust when Maggie tells him of her love for Philip.

2 Why does Maggie promise not see Philip again?

Section 3

1 How are the different personalities of Tom and Philip revealed in the Red Deeps?

2 Analyse the language Tom uses against Philip. How would you describe it?

Section 4

1 How does Maggie react against her brother?

2 At the end of the chapter Maggie 'felt a kind of relief'. Why?

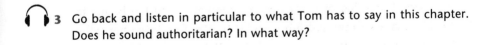

3 Go back and listen in particular to what Tom has to say in this chapter. Does he sound authoritarian? In what way?

CHAPTER 20

A day of reckoning [1]

Three weeks later, at the prettiest time of the year when Dorlcote Mill was surrounded by blossoming trees, green grass and daisies, Tom Tulliver came home earlier than usual.

'You're early, Tom! Why is that?' asked his father.

'I have a surprise for you, Father,' said Tom, with shining eyes. 'I have been doing some business of my own that you don't know about. And I have managed to save three hundred and twenty pounds. Now we can pay off the creditors!'

Mrs Tulliver threw her arms around Tom's neck and cried, 'Oh, my boy! I knew you would save us in the end!' But Mr Tulliver just sat silent, unable to speak. Tom and Maggie were both afraid that the news had been too much for him. But then he began to weep. He wept quietly for a long time, then he wiped his face and held out his hand to Tom.

'Shake hands with me, my boy!' he said. 'I'm proud of you!'

Tom shook his father's hand. It was the greatest triumph of his life. Maggie forgot her own sorrows for a moment and felt happy for Tom. She admired him and felt grateful to him for giving her father this great pleasure. It compensated for all his faults, whereas she had done nothing fine to compensate for her own faults. She did not feel jealous of Tom, even though, for the first time, he seemed more important to her father than she did.

There was much more talk before they went to bed. Mr Tulliver wanted to know all the details of Tom's trading adventures. Tom

---

1. **day of reckoning** : day on which earlier problems are resolved.

told him the whole story, then said, 'My uncle Deane has written to all the creditors and asked them to meet us tomorrow at the Golden Lion Hotel. He has ordered a dinner for them. There was an announcement in the newspaper.'

'Then Wakem knows of it!' said Mr Tulliver, with triumph in his eyes.

The next day he was very excited: his cheeks were red and his eyes glittered. At two o'clock, he was seated with the creditors at a long table in the Golden Lion Hotel.

When Mr Tulliver rose to make his speech, he seemed his former self: proud, confident, warm-hearted and hot-tempered. He spoke about his bad luck and alluded to the scoundrels [1] who had ruined him, but then he spoke about Tom's trading, and his voice was full of fatherly pride and pleasure. Mr Deane made a speech and proposed a toast to [2] Tom's health. Then Tom himself made the only speech of his life. He said he was glad he had been able to help his father and restore his family's good name, and he hoped he would never do anything to disgrace that name. It was a very short and simple speech, but the audience applauded it enthusiastically, and Mr Tulliver starting telling the people seated next to him that he had spent a great deal of money on his son's education.

The party broke up at five o'clock. Tom stayed in St Ogg's to attend to some business. Mr Tulliver mounted his horse and rode home to tell Mrs Tulliver and Maggie about all the memorable things that had been said and done. He rode slowly down the main street with his head held high. As he approached Dorlcote Mill, he saw Wakem on horseback coming towards him. 'Tulliver!' said Wakem sharply. 'Where have you been? I've been waiting for you for an hour to do the accounts!'

'Get somebody else to do them, then!' cried Mr Tulliver.

---

1. **scoundrels** : people with no moral conscience or principles.
2. **a toast to** : a drink in honour of.

'You have been drinking, I suppose,' said Wakem, noticing Mr Tulliver's flushed face and glittering eyes.

'No. I don't need drink to help me decide that I won't work for a scoundrel.'

'Very well! You may leave the mill tomorrow. Let me pass.'

Mr Tulliver had placed his horse in front of the gate, so that Wakem's horse could not get out. 'No, I shall not let you pass. I'll tell you what I think of you first! You are a scoundrel, I say!'

'Let me pass, you ignorant brute!' cried Wakem.

Mr Tulliver raised his whip and rushed forward. Wakem's horse reared, [1] and Wakem fell to the ground. Before he had time to get up, Mr Tulliver got off his horse and whipped him fiercely on the back. Wakem shouted for help, then a woman screamed and a voice cried out, 'Father! Father!' At last Mr Tulliver dropped his whip.

Maggie helped Wakem onto his horse, while Mrs Tulliver stood, frightened and pale, at the door. Then Wakem turned to Mr Tulliver and said, 'You'll suffer for this, Sir!'

'I don't care!' cried Mr Tulliver. 'Go and show your back in town, and tell them I thrashed you! Tell them I've made things a bit more even in the world!'

As Wakem rode off in a rage, Mr Tulliver grasped Maggie's arm. 'I feel ill,' he said. 'I feel faint. Help me into the house. I have a pain in my head.'

Mr Tulliver lay ill in bed all that evening. In the night, the pain in his head was very bad, and he asked his wife to call Tom and Maggie.

'I don't think I will get up from this bed again,' he said. 'This world has been too much for me. But you have done well, Tom, and I thank you for it. I have just one more wish. Try to get the old mill back.'

'I will, Father,' said Tom.

---

1. **reared** : rose up.

'And take care of your mother and sister.'

Mr Tulliver turned his eyes on Maggie. She knelt down by the bed and held his hand.

'Don't worry, my girl,' said Mr Tulliver. 'You will find someone who will love you and take care of you. Be good to her, Tom! Come, Bessy, and kiss me! Come, Maggie.'

He lay quietly for a little while, then he said, 'I had my turn – I thrashed him! It was only fair.'

'But, Father,' said Maggie, bending close to him. 'You can forgive him now, can't you?'

'No, Maggie, I don't forgive him... You can't love a scoundrel... This world's been... too much for me...'

He fell silent then, and an hour later he was dead.

When Tom and Maggie went downstairs, they looked at their father's empty chair in the pale morning light. 'Tom, forgive me,' said Maggie. 'Let's always love each other!' She put her arms around his neck, and they wept together.

A C T I V I T I E S

1 What are the three main events in this chapter?

2 Mr Tulliver appears to be 'his former self'. Why does this prove to be fateful?

3 Imagine you witnessed the fight between Mr Tulliver and Wakem. Write a short description. Remember past narrative forms ('*I was walking down the street when suddenly I saw...*').

4 The repayment of the family's debts and the death of their father appear to have brought Tom and Maggie closer together. What aspects of their personalities could bring conflict in the future?

PART 3

1 In chapter 15, exercise 4b you were asked to describe a place which is important to you. Using the vocabulary you built up, write a short description of the place and explain why it is important to you (around 200 words).

2 In chapter 17, exercise 2 you wrote a short letter to Maggie giving her advice on the basis of the arguments presented in the chapter. In many magazines there is a person who replies to readers' problems (sentimental, professional, economic). Do you ever read these pages?

3 Imagine Tom has written to you telling you about his problems with Maggie. What advice would you give him? Compare your ideas with other students in a group. Remember the advice structures which you reviewed in chapter 17 (*If I were you I'd...*, *I think you should... I would...*).

Now write the letter using not more than 200 words expressing your opinion.

4 In chapter 19 'Maggie blushed red and felt her hands trembling' with fear of her relationship with Philip being discovered. Think of a moment when you were afraid. Tell your partner about it.

5 Write a short summary of the main events in part 3 as you did for parts 1 and 2. Try to use between 100 and 150 words.

The 'woman question' in Victorian Britain

In nineteenth-century Britain, men and women of the lower social classes worked side by side in fields, factories, and the houses of the rich. Working-class women were expected to earn a living, though they were paid substantially less than men for the same work. Many people of the urban and rural working classes were illiterate, but what little learning they had was distributed equally between men and women. Among the aristocracy, gentry, and middle classes, however, gender differences were extreme. Until the late 1860s, the daughters of these classes were taught little except reading, writing, and 'accomplishments' (music, dancing, drawing, sewing and French). Their brothers were taught Latin, Greek and Euclid at school, and they could go on to university. With this education, a young gentleman could find a rewarding profession, whereas his sister's 'accomplishments' could only be used to attract a husband. If absolutely necessary, she could find work as a governess but, if she did so, she sacrificed her class status. A governess was supposed to be a 'gentlewoman', but the fact that she had to earn her living put her class status into question.

A 'real lady' did not work. Her life was passed in the family circle. While she was young and unmarried, she was never left alone in male company. Chastity and a clear sense of 'a woman's place' were the signs of the true lady. When she married, her father would give a sum of money to her husband. If this dowry [1] was a large fortune, she could expect many young men to court her. If, on the other hand, her father could not afford a dowry, her chances of marriage were slim. Any money that she brought to

---

1. **dowry** [dauəri] : money or property that a woman's parents give to the man she marries.

A Life Well Spent (1862) by Charles West Cope.
Private collection.

This painting gives a clear idea of the role
of 'good women' in the Victorian Age.

the marriage immediately became the property of her husband. The story of Maggie Tulliver is set in the early nineteenth century, but the novel was published in 1860. By that time, the 'woman question' had become an important subject of public debate. The central issues were education and work; only the most radical Victorian feminists argued that women should be allowed to vote. In the 1860s, the first serious private girls' schools were opened, offering girls of the ruling classes the same kind of education that their brothers received at Eton and Harrow. At the same time, the first women's colleges were opened at Oxford and Cambridge Universities. These new schools and colleges were not only an advance in girls' education but also in women's work: educated women could now become teachers and administrators in prestigious institutions like Girton College, Cambridge. During the Crimean War, in the 1850s, Florence Nightingale had set a brilliant example of female excellence in nursing, and many women followed her into the profession. In the 1870s, the spreading use of the typewriter meant that male copyists (who copied documents by hand in law offices, for example) were rapidly replaced by female secretaries. In the course of twenty years then, from 1855 to 1875, three professions –

nursing, teaching, and secretarial work – became widely available to women.

The Second Reform Act, designed to extend the British electorate, was enacted in 1867. The philosopher and Liberal Member of Parliament, John Stuart Mill, presented a petition to the House, proposing that the word 'men' be changed to 'people' in the Second Reform Act. The petition was ignored, and women did not get the vote until 1918, but the petition showed, for the first time, that there was wide support for the women's vote.

Finally, the Married Women's Property Acts of 1870 and 1882 gave married women control of their own property for the first time. All these changes came too late for girls like Maggie Tulliver, but George Eliot lived to see them and to become herself a shining example of the successful professional woman. She had overcome enormous disadvantages: she was born female; her family were in the upper echelons [1] of the rural working class; and she lived her early life in the provinces, far from the artistic and intellectual influences of London. Nevertheless, despite these initial disadvantages, by the 1870s she was generally accepted as the greatest novelist of her generation.

---

1. **echelons** [eʃəlɒnz] : levels.

'To understand how people really lived, ranging from the minutiae of everyday life to the great questions of the day, you need go no further than fiction.'

Maggie's situation is typical of early Victorian women but her behaviour can be seen as a reason why the condition of women was destined to change. Why?

CHAPTER ◆ 21

A duet in paradise

Two years have passed. The large, comfortable drawing room, with an open grand piano and a pleasant view across the garden to a boathouse on the River Floss, is Mr Deane's. The neat little lady, wearing a black dress and working on her embroidery, [1] is Lucy Deane. The fine young man who is snapping [2] the scissors in the face of a small dog by Lucy's feet is Mr Stephen Guest, the son of the owner of Guest and Company. He wears a diamond ring and, though it is noon, he is a little sleepy.

'Give me my scissors, please,' said Lucy, holding out her little shell-pink palm. 'And stop teasing [3] Minnie. I have some news for you.'

'What news?' asked Stephen. He was a handsome young man of twenty-five, with dark-brown hair and an affectionate ironic expression in his eyes.

'Guess! It is something I mentioned to you not long ago.'

'But you have mentioned many things to me not long ago. How can I possibly guess?'

'Yes, I know you think I am silly.'

'I think you are perfectly charming.'

'And my silliness makes part of my charm?'

---

1. **embroidery** : cloth decorated with patterns sewn in thread of various colours.
2. **snapping** : rapidly opening and closing.
3. **teasing** : provoking.

'I didn't say that.'

'But I know you like women to be silly. Philip Wakem told me a few days ago, when you were not here.'

'Well, that is Philip's opinion. He is always talking about it. I think he must be in love with some unknown lady who is not silly at all.'

'I wonder if Maggie will refuse to see Philip, as her brother does,' said Lucy. 'I hope not. If she does, we won't be able to sing together as usual.'

'What? Is your cousin coming to stay with you?' asked Stephen, with a look of slight annoyance.

'Yes, that was my news. She has just left the school she has been teaching at for the past two years, poor thing, ever since her father died. And she is coming to stay with me for a month or two. I'm so happy. I love my cousin Maggie best of all the girls I know.'

'And I suppose you will be inseparable, and I will have no chance to talk to you alone, unless we find a lover for her. Why won't she like Philip?'

'Maggie's father hated Philip's father. Papa told me there was a dreadful quarrel the day before my uncle died. Papa says that my uncle was wrong to hate Mr Wakem so, but naturally Tom and Maggie don't like to be reminded of those things. They have had so much trouble. Maggie has probably had no pleasure at all since her father died. She went to work in that dreary 1 school because she wanted to be independent. She didn't want to go and live with aunt Glegg, and I couldn't invite her here, because Mama was so ill and everything was so sad. That's why I have invited her now. I want her to have a long holiday.'

'That's very sweet and angelic of you,' said Stephen, with an admiring smile. 'Especially if she is anything like her mother.'

'Poor Aunt! You are cruel to ridicule her. She was a great help to

---

1. **dreary** : depressing.

me during Mama's illness. And she runs the house much better than a stranger would.'

'Her cakes are excellent, I admit,' said Stephen, 'but her conversation is a bore. Her daughter will be fat and blonde, I suppose, and will sit staring at us silently.'

Lucy laughed and clapped her hands, 'Oh yes!' she cried. 'My cousin Maggie is exactly like that! You must have met her already.'

'No, indeed. I am only guessing what Mrs Tulliver's daughter must be like. And, if she won't let Philip come, we shall be even more bored.'

Lucy reached her hand out to get the scissors, but Stephen caught it and put it to his lips. Little Lucy felt very proud and happy. She knew that Stephen loved her, although they had not yet spoken of marriage. That is the sweetest moment of courtship, when every word and gesture is full of hidden meaning.

'You are very clever,' said Lucy, 'to have guessed what Maggie is like. She could have been like Tom. He isn't fat at all, and he certainly doesn't stare at people.'

'No he doesn't. He seems as proud as Lucifer, and rather unfriendly.'

'I like Tom. He gave me Minnie as a present, you know. Papa says Tom is an excellent young man.'

'Yes. I heard your father and mine discussing young Tulliver one night at dinner. They said he did something wonderful for the Company. What was it, now? Oh, yes. He rode home all the way from London without stopping to warn them about something important to do with business. If he hadn't, they would have lost a lot of money. I can't remember what it was exactly. I was rather sleepy at the time.'

Stephen went to the piano and started humming [1] a tune. 'Come and sing this song with me, Lucy,' he said.

'Philip says that is just a sentimental love song,' said Lucy. 'He

---

1. **humming** : singing to himself.

doesn't like it at all.'

'Well, Philip is the fallen Adam, whereas we are Adam and Eve in paradise before the Fall.'[1]

Lucy sat at the piano and began to play. Lovers who sing together never have doubts and fears. The silvery soprano and the deep bass blend[2] so well together that the lovers themselves seem to be in perfect harmony. Lucy and Stephen felt very happy as they finished their song, and Stephen rose to leave.

'I suppose you will be busy with your cousin tomorrow,' said Stephen, smiling down at Lucy. 'But may I come the next day?'

'Oh, yes! Come and meet my cousin Maggie. But I'm sure you have met her before, you described her so well.'

---

1. **Philip ... Fall** : Philip is unhappy while we are happy.
2. **blend** : harmonise.

A   C   T   I   V   I   T   I   E   S

1 In chapter 21 the story has moved forward two years and people's lives have changed. What changes have there been in Maggie and Mrs Tulliver's lives?

2 Use the three columns to identify the relations between the characters in chapter 21. Check you understand the words in column 3 before you start!

Stephen is	Lucy's	aunt
Lucy is	Maggie's	brother
Maggie is	Stephen's	cousin
Tom is	Mrs Tulliver's	daughter
Mrs Tulliver is	Mr Deane's	lover
		mother
		niece
		nephew
		sister-in-law
		son

Example: Lucy is Maggie's cousin

3 What are Stephen's opinions of Lucy's family? Match the adjectives to the name.

Adjectives: boring, proud, unfriendly
Name: Tom, Mrs Tulliver

4 What are **your** first impressions of Stephen? Compare your impressions with your partner.

5 The relationship between Stephen and Lucy appears idyllic ('Lovers who sing together never have doubts and fears.') What do you think will happen in the next chapter?

6 What trick does Lucy play on Stephen?

CHAPTER 22

First impressions

H e is very clever, Maggie,' said Lucy, as they sat together in the drawing room. 'I am sure you will like him.'

Maggie smiled at her and stroked her hair. 'I shall be very difficult to please,' she said. 'A gentleman who thinks he is good enough for you must expect to be sharply criticised.'

'I think he is too good for me. Sometimes, when he's away, I can't believe that he loves me. But I never doubt it when he is with me.' Lucy paused and looked at her cousin. 'You know, Maggie, I would never tell anyone else these things, but I want to tell you.'

'Well, if I don't approve of him, you can give him up, since you're not engaged,' said Maggie playfully.

'I'm glad we're not engaged,' said Lucy. 'Everything is so perfect now. I don't want anything to change. Sometimes I'm afraid that Stephen will say he has spoken to Papa. I know that Papa expects it. And Stephen's sisters are very nice to me now. They weren't at first, and it's not surprising. It does seem strange to think I might live in a great house – Park House, you know, is Stephen's home. I'm such an insignificant little thing.'

'You don't need to be large yourself to live in a large house,' said Maggie, laughing. 'Are Mr Guest's sisters large?'

'Oh no – and not handsome either. But he is,' said Lucy, blushing pink. 'Everyone thinks so.'

'And what do you think?' asked Maggie.

'I don't want to raise your expectations [1] too much, or you might be disappointed. When you meet, I will have a good laugh. I have

---

1. **raise your expectations** : give you false hopes.

played a joke on him, but I won't tell you what it is.' She looked thoughtfully at Maggie for a few moments, then she said, 'What witchcraft 1 do you use, Maggie, to make you look best in plain old clothes. Now if I wore plain clothes I would look plain myself. No one would notice me. In fact, I think I will go and change my dress. Stephen will be here soon.'

When Lucy had gone upstairs, Maggie went to the French windows 2 and breathed in the fresh spring air. Outside, the grass was full of wild flowers and the dear old River Floss looked silver in the distance. The air was sweet with the scent 3 of flowers, and the birds were singing. Maggie's eyes filled with tears. The sight of the Floss filled her with memories, some pleasant but many painful. Her future, she thought, was likely to be worse than her past. And Maggie could no longer stop wishing for a better life. She remembered the years of contented renunciation. Perhaps it would be better if she were still like that. But she had slipped back into desire and longing. She found her joyless life harder and harder to bear. She imagined other better lives more and more clearly.

Maggie heard the door open behind her and quickly wiped away her tears.

'I hope you still play the piano, Maggie,' said Lucy brightly, appearing in a very pretty new dress. 'You were so much better than I was at Miss Firniss's school.'

'Yes, I still play,' said Maggie.

'And do you like to sing? Stephen and I love singing more than anything.'

'Yes, I like it very much,' said Maggie, smiling.

'Oh, good! We will have a wonderful time singing, then. That is, if you don't feel exactly as Tom does.'

---

1. **witchcraft** : the use of magic powers, especially evil ones.
2. **French windows** : windows that extend down to the floor, like a door.
3. **scent** : smell.

'You can be certain I don't feel exactly as Tom does,' said Maggie.

'About one thing in particular, I mean. I know Tom does not like Philip Wakem, and will never enter a room if Philip is there. But there are so few musical gentlemen in St Ogg's. Philip and Stephen and I have great fun singing together. But I won't invite him if it would upset you.'

'I don't feel as Tom does at all on that subject,' said Maggie. 'I've always liked Philip.'

'Oh, I'm so glad!' said Lucy. 'Then you won't mind him coming sometimes. I'm very fond of poor Philip. I just wish he were not so sensitive about his deformity. I suppose it is his deformity that makes him so sad – and sometimes bitter. It is certainly very pitiful to see his poor little crooked body and pale face among great strong people...'

Maggie was just about to interrupt her when the doorbell rang.

'Ah! That must be Stephen!'

It was too late for Maggie to speak now. The door opened, and Minnie growled a little as a tall gentleman entered. He went up to Lucy and took her hand with a tender glance. [1] He clearly had not noticed that there was someone else in the room.

'Let me introduce you to my cousin Miss Tulliver,' said Lucy, turning towards Maggie with a smile. 'This is Mr Stephen Guest.'

For a moment, Stephen could not conceal his surprise at the sight of this tall, dark-eyed nymph with her crown of black hair. He blushed and bowed [2] to her. Maggie felt suddenly timid. Causing a tall handsome man to blush was a new experience for her, and it was very pleasant – so pleasant that it almost made her forget her previous emotion about Philip. There was a new brightness in her eyes and a blush on her cheek as she sat down and took up her sewing.

'I hope you see how right you were in your description of her the

---

1. **glance** : look.
2. **bowed** [baʊd] : bent his head as a sign of respect.

day before yesterday!' said Lucy, with a pretty laugh of triumph.

'Your cousin has deceived me, Miss Tulliver,' said Stephen, playing with the dog to hide his confusion. 'She said you had blonde hair and blue eyes.'

'Indeed I did not!' laughed Lucy. 'You said so!'

'I wish I could always be wrong in the same way,' said Stephen, 'and find reality so much more beautiful than my preconceptions.'

'A very pretty speech,' said Maggie, looking at him defiantly. It was clear that he had been ridiculing her the other day. 'You know exactly what you have to say to get yourself out of an embarrassing situation.'

Lucy had said that he liked to ridicule people, and Maggie thought he was probably conceited as well. Stephen, meanwhile, thought that Maggie had a bit of the devil in her. He wished she would look at him again. 'Sometimes,' he said, 'the words you have to say happen to be true.'

'Sometimes,' said Maggie, 'but not often.'

Lucy was alarmed. She thought Stephen and Maggie were not going to like each other. She had been afraid that Maggie would be too strange and clever to please Stephen. 'Why Maggie,' she said. 'You always told me that you were too fond of being admired, and now you are angry because someone admires you.'

Maggie began to feel ashamed of herself. She was not used to social situations. She could not take things lightly, as other people did. Stephen, noticing her confusion, changed the subject and began to talk about his plans to run as a candidate in the next election. But all the time he was thinking of Maggie. He had heard that her father had gone bankrupt. She must be very poor, he thought, but that only made her more interesting, more unlike other women he knew. 'My father wants me to become a Member of Parliament very much, and gifts like mine' – here Stephen put his large white hands through his dark brown hair with playful self-admiration – 'involve responsibilities. Don't you think so, Miss Tulliver?'

Maggie's face was bent over her sewing, but he could see that she was smiling. 'Yes. Your self-confidence and ability to talk should not be wasted in drawing rooms alone,' she said.

She doesn't look at me when I talk about myself, he thought. I must try another subject. He began to tell them about a book he had read recently. It is always pleasant to improve the minds of ladies by talking to them on subjects of which they know nothing. It was a fascinating book, Stephen told them, about geology. As he described it, Maggie put down her sewing and looked at him, bending forward attentively. He was so fascinated by her large, dark eyes that he forgot to look occasionally towards Lucy. But Lucy was perfectly happy. She was glad that Stephen was showing Maggie how clever he was. Perhaps they would be friends after all.

'Shall I bring you the book, Miss Tulliver?'

'Oh! Thank you,' said Maggie.

'No, no,' said Lucy. 'Don't bring her the book. If she starts reading, she will never stop. And I want her to have delicious do-nothing days, just talking and riding and boating. That's the sort of holiday she needs.'

'Shall we go out in a boat on the river now?' asked Stephen.

Maggie and Lucy agreed, and Maggie went out to find her coat and hat. As soon as they were alone, Lucy told Stephen that Maggie had no objection to seeing Philip.

'Well, I'll bring him tomorrow evening,' said Stephen.

'Yes, please do,' said Lucy. 'And you do like Maggie, don't you? She's such a sweet, handsome girl.'

'She's too tall,' said Stephen, smiling down at Lucy, 'and too hot-tempered. She's not my type of woman at all.'

Lucy did not doubt the truth of what Stephen said. Stephen, meanwhile, was thinking that a boat-ride would be perfect. Maggie would have to take his hand at least twice: once to get into the boat and once to get out. Had he fallen in love with Maggie at first sight? Certainly not. Those things do not happen in real life. Besides, he was in love already: he was almost engaged to the sweetest girl in the world. It was perfectly natural and safe to admire beauty and enjoy looking at it. And there was really something interesting about Maggie, with her poverty and her troubles. Usually Stephen did not like women with strong characters, but Maggie's strength of character fascinated him. It was interesting to talk to such women, so long as you did not have to marry them.

Maggie did not look at him as he rowed the boat. She looked at the old familiar banks of the Floss. She felt lonely. She missed Philip, the only person who had ever loved her as she longed to be loved. But after a while, she asked Stephen if he would teach her how to row the boat. Stephen was very glad to do so. Rowing the boat made Maggie's eyes shine and her cheeks flush.

'I enjoyed that very much!' said Maggie, as she stepped out of the boat, but she did not look where she was putting her foot and she slipped. Luckily Mr Stephen Guest was holding her hand at that moment to help her out of the boat. He gripped her tightly and helped her onto the bank.

'I hope you are not hurt?' he said, bending to look at her face with anxiety. Maggie found it very pleasant to be protected like that by someone taller and stronger than herself.

When they reached home again, they found Mr and Mrs Glegg sitting with Mrs Tulliver in the drawing room. Stephen asked if he could come again in the evening, then he hurried away.

1 Put these events from chapter 22 into the correct order:

a ☐ Maggie feels the need for a better life.

b ☐ Lucy tells Maggie of her intention to invite Philip.

c ☐ Maggie, Lucy and Stephen go rowing on the Floss.

d ☐ Stephen and Maggie meet for the first time.

e ☐ Lucy tells Maggie about Stephen.

2 Are there any other events you would add?

3 Stephen is conceited and Maggie is clever. Complete the table with examples from the chapter. Two examples have been done for you.

Stephen's conceit	Maggie's intelligence
• '…gifts like mine involve responsibilities'	• 'You don't need to be large yourself to live in a large house. Are Mr Guest's sisters large?'
•	•
•	•

4 Maggie and Stephen are very different but they are instantly attracted to each other. Why? Discuss your ideas with your partner.

5 Lucy plans to invite Philip for an evening together. What problems will this cause Maggie?

CHAPTER 23

Maggie tells her secret

W hen Maggie went up to her bedroom that night, she felt very excited. She walked up and down her room with shining eyes and flushed cheeks. Had anything remarkable happened? Not really. She had heard some fine music and listened to a fine bass voice. She had noticed that Stephen looked at her often, and that his glance seemed as deep and resonant as his voice. These things would be nothing to a well-educated young lady with a perfectly balanced mind, who had all the advantages of fortune and refined society. But, if Maggie had been that young lady, you would probably never have heard her story. Her life would have been so untroubled that no one would have written about it, for the happiest women, like the happiest nations, have no history.

Maggie had a hungry nature, and she had just come from a life with no joy or excitement in it. These apparently trivial things excited her in a way that was a mystery even to herself. She did not think specifically of Mr Stephen Guest or of the signs that he admired her; she just felt the presence of a world of love and beauty and delight, made up of images from all the poetry and romance she had ever read.

These thoughts were interrupted by Lucy: 'Oh, good, you are not in bed yet! I wanted to talk a little before going to sleep. Did you enjoy the music this evening, Maggie?'

'Oh, yes,' said Maggie, 'that is why I am not sleepy. Music makes me feel so alive.'

'And Stephen has a splendid voice, hasn't he?'

'I don't think either of us should judge that,' said Maggie, laughing as she brushed her long black hair. 'You are not impartial, and I have not heard music for so long that I think I would find any voice splendid.'

'But tell me what you think of him, now,' said Lucy eagerly, sitting beside her. 'Tell me exactly: the good and the bad too.'

'I think you should humiliate him a little. A lover should not be so self-confident. He should tremble more.'

'Nonsense, Maggie! I couldn't make anyone tremble! I see you think he is conceited, but you don't dislike him, do you?'

'No! How could I dislike anyone who promised to make you happy?'

'We shall have more music tomorrow evening. Stephen will bring Philip.'

'Oh, Lucy! I can't see him,' said Maggie, turning pale. 'Not without Tom's permission.'

'Tell him it was my fault,' said Lucy.

'But I promised him that I would not speak to Philip. I don't want to quarrel with Tom again.'

'How unreasonable!' said Lucy. 'What can poor Philip have done? May I speak to Tom about it?'

'No, no. I'll ask him tomorrow.'

'Maggie,' said Lucy. 'Don't keep secrets from me. I keep none from you.'

'I would like to tell you,' said Maggie, 'but don't mention it to anyone, least of all to Philip himself or to Mr Stephen Guest.'

Maggie told Lucy the whole story. Never before had she known the relief of telling someone about her most intimate life. Lucy listened, her sweet face bent towards Maggie's with sympathetic interest. At last she said, 'It is very beautiful that you love Philip. I never thought he would have such happiness. And, in my opinion, you should not give up. There are obstacles now, but they can be overcome in time.'

Maggie shook her head.

'Yes, yes,' said Lucy. 'There's something romantic about it, something so unusual. Philip will adore you like a husband in a fairy tale. I shall think of a way to make everyone agree, so that you can marry Philip when I marry – someone else.'

Maggie tried to smile, but shivered, [1] as if she felt a sudden chill. [2]

'Ah, dear, you are cold,' said Lucy. 'You must go to bed.'

They kissed each other, and Lucy went away.

---

1. **shivered** : shook slightly from the cold.
2. **chill** : cold air.

A   C   T   I   V   I   T   I   E   S

1 Fill each of the spaces in this short text with **one** suitable word from the box below.

Maggie was a..................... by the evening of music she had spent with Stephen and Lucy after so long b.................... love and beauty. The other 'voice' that Maggie had tried to c.................... now made her realise how unhappy and lonely she had been. Her d.................... to Tom never to see Philip again, however, represented clear evidence of the practical e.................... of reconciling the two f.................... of her personality. Her sense of g.................... to her family and the promise she had h.................... meant that she would ask her brother for i.................... to see Philip. The voice of self-sacrifice seemed again to have j.................... .

> problems   loyalty   made   permission   promise
> excited   sides   suppress   without   won

2 'Maggie tried to smile, but shivered, as if she felt a sudden chill.' Why do you think Maggie reacted in this way when Lucy imagines Maggie marrying Philip?

3 In chapter 24, Maggie goes to ask Tom permission to see Philip. What do you think Tom's reaction will be?

Brother and sister

Tom lived in rented rooms in town. Maggie went there at lunch time, because she knew that the rest of the day he was at work. Sad memories came back to Maggie as she entered the small sitting room, which was now all that Tom could call home. Home had once meant something very different: a familiar place full of familiar objects they had known and loved since childhood.

'I didn't expect to see you, Maggie,' said Tom.

'I had to come to ask you something,' said Maggie, trembling.

Tom's voice was colder as he answered, 'What is it?'

'I want to see Philip Wakem,' said Maggie. 'Don't be angry. It's not my fault. You see, Philip is a friend of Lucy's, and Lucy has invited him to the house this evening. I told her I could not see him without asking you first. I promise there will never be anything secret between me and Philip again.'

Tom frowned and turned away from her. 'You know how I feel about that, Maggie,' he said. 'While my father was alive, I tried to prevent you from disgracing the family as well as yourself. Now I must let you choose, but if you think of Philip Wakem as a lover, I will never speak to you again.'

'I don't think of him as a lover, dear Tom. I know it would lead to misery. But I will soon go away to work in another school, and I would like to be friends with him while I am here. Lucy wishes it.'

Tom looked a little less severe: he always liked to do what Lucy wished. 'I don't mind you seeing him occasionally at my uncle Deane's house. But I have no confidence in you, Maggie.'

Maggie's lip began to tremble, and tears came into her eyes. 'Why do you say that, Tom? It is very cruel of you. I have kept my promise.

My life has been difficult as well as yours.'

Tom put his hand gently on her arm and said, 'I didn't mean to be unkind, Maggie. It's just that you always go to extremes. You have no judgement and self-control. But you think you know best, so you won't listen to me. You know I didn't want you to go to work in that school. Aunt Glegg was willing to let you live with her. I wanted you to be a lady. I wanted to take care of you, as my father desired, until you found a suitable husband.'

'Yes – I know – dear Tom,' said Maggie, trying to control her tears. 'I am grateful to you. I know you want only what is best for me. But you can't judge what is best for me, because we are so different.'

'I know we are different. It's hard for me to understand how you could have ever thought of Philip Wakem as a lover. Even if it were not disgusting to me in any other way, I would still object to you marrying a man whose father must hate us. As I say, Maggie, you go to extremes. One moment you take pleasure in a perverse self-denial, the next moment you have not the strength to resist doing something that you know is wrong.'

Maggie felt as if Tom was holding up a mirror in which all her faults were reflected. But she judged him too. She thought that he was narrow and unjust. His needs were simple, and he could not understand hers.

'I can't make you think better of me, Tom. But I do understand your feelings. I see as well as you do that Philip and I can never be married. I am telling you the truth, and you should believe me.'

'All right, Maggie. Let's not talk about it any more. I don't mind if you see Philip at our uncle's house. I believe what you say – or at least I know that you believe it. I'm only warning you. I want to be a good brother to you, if you will let me.'

'I know,' said Maggie, then she kissed his cheek and left him.

1 The differences between Tom and Maggie are confirmed in this chapter. Whose side are you on? Collect examples from chapter 24 in support of Tom and Maggie. Some examples both in favour and against Tom have been done for you and two have been put into the appropriate column. Put the others into the correct column and then do the same for Maggie. Add any others which you think are appropriate.

In favour of Tom	In favour of Maggie
• Tom genuinely loves his sister and wants what he believes is best for her	• Tom has never been able to accept his sister's personality
•	•
•	•
•	•
•	•
	•
	•
	•

a Tom stubbornly insists on knowing what is right for his sister
b Tom's feelings of hatred and disgust for Philip are unacceptable
c Tom perceptively exposes his sister's contradictory personality
d Tom is obsessed with the good name of the family
e Tom's reaction to Maggie's relationship with Philip was cruel and insensitive
f Tom has also suffered as a result of the financial problems brought on by his father

2 Role-play development

Work in groups of three. Student A will defend Tom; student B will support Maggie; student C will act as a spokesperson who will manage the debate. (In chapter 4, exercise 4 you were asked to take sides: defending either Mr Tulliver or Mrs Glegg.)

CHAPTER 25

Under a spell [1]

P hilip did not come with Stephen that evening. He had
left a note saying that he would be away for two weeks.
Maggie had been very anxious about seeing him again,
and she was not sorry that the meeting must be deferred. [2]

During those two weeks, Maggie was introduced to the life of a
young lady in high society. She went to parties and was much
admired by the gentlemen and envied by the ladies for her fine
figure and her fine dark eyes. Stephen's sisters invited her with Lucy
to Park House. They found her manners a little strange, but that did
not displease them. Her beauty was superior to theirs, so they were
quite glad to find her manners inferior.

Maggie enjoyed getting up every morning with nothing particular
to do. She enjoyed playing the piano and going for walks in the
spring sunshine. This new life was very pleasant, and pleasant
thoughts began gradually to replace her sad memories and worries
about the future.

Stephen Guest was always at Lucy's side. Lucy was very happy.
Stephen had become much more interesting since Maggie arrived.
Quiet little Lucy listened to their discussions with great interest.
When Maggie marries Philip, she thought, the four of us will be
friends forever. Lucy did not feel at all jealous. It did not worry her
that Stephen addressed almost all his remarks to Maggie. She knew
that Stephen loved her. He always sat beside her, and he was just as
kind and tender to her as he had been before. In fact, he seemed
even more so.

---

1. **spell** : magic.
2. **deferred** : postponed.

Stephen himself was not aware that he took Lucy's arm or kissed her hand more often than he had done before: it was an unconscious act of conscience. He and Maggie hardly ever touched each other or stood close to each other. If Lucy left them alone in the drawing room, Stephen would look at a book or a sheet of music, and Maggie would become absorbed in her sewing. They would wait in silence until Lucy returned, each intensely aware of the other's presence. When Lucy was back in the room, they could relax, and the conversation could begin again. Maggie could contradict Stephen and laugh at him, and Stephen could tell her, with playful irony, that she should have more respect for the intelligence of men. Neither of them wondered what all this might mean.

On the day of Philip's return, Lucy said she had to go out in the evening to see a friend who was ill. Stephen was there when Lucy made this announcement. There was a tacit agreement that he would not return in the evening, as he usually did.

After dinner, when Lucy was gone, Maggie sat alone in the drawing room, with Minnie on her lap, [1] stroking the dog's silky ears. Suddenly she heard the sound of footsteps on the gravel outside. Looking through the French window, she saw Mr Stephen Guest walking up the garden path, coming straight from the river. Maggie's heart began to beat fast.

Stephen came up to the French window, with a roll of sheet music in his hand. 'Hello,' he said, blushing. 'You are surprised to see me, Miss Tulliver. I was just rowing past in my boat, so I thought I would leave some music for your cousin. I forgot to bring it this morning. Will you give it to her?'

'Yes,' said Maggie.

Stephen came in through the French window and put the music on the piano, then he sat down beside Maggie. He had never done so before. Stephen leaned over and began to stroke Minnie's ears,

---

1. **lap** : knees.

but he could think of nothing to say. He kept stroking the dog slowly. It was like an action in a dream. He wanted to look at Maggie, but he did not dare. He thought that if he could look into her eyes for a long time he would be satisfied. Maggie, meanwhile, kept her eyes fixed on the dog, unable to look up.

At last Stephen said, 'Do you like sitting alone?'

Maggie looked at him, smiled, and said, 'It wouldn't be polite for me to say "yes", would it?'

Stephen laughed, delighted that she was looking at him. 'No, I suppose it wouldn't,' he said.

Maggie looked out of window, and they were silent once more. 'I wish Lucy could have stayed in this evening,' she said after a while. 'We could have played music.'

'We shall play and sing tomorrow night, and we shall have a tenor,' said Stephen. 'Philip is back. I saw him as I was going home this morning. Will you tell your cousin?'

The mention of Philip's name broke the spell. Maggie rose from her chair suddenly, put Minnie down on a cushion, and took up her sewing. Then she sat in another chair, farther away from him. Stephen was disappointed. He felt foolish for having come. He thought she must know that he had missed his dinner at home and come in the hope of finding her alone.

'Well, good-bye,' said Stephen.

Maggie thought perhaps she had been rude. 'Won't you stay?' she asked timidly, looking up at him.

'No, thank you,' said Stephen. 'I must go. Please remember to tell your cousin that I brought the music.'

'Yes.' She was looking at him still, and his eyes had a serious and longing expression.

'And that Philip is back.'

'Yes.' (Maggie did not notice Philip's name this time.)

'Will you walk down to the river with me?' asked Stephen in a gentle voice. Maggie rose and came to his side, but he felt disappointed because she was no longer looking at him. 'Take my arm,' he said, in a low tone, as if it were a secret.

Most women find the offer of a man's arm charming. They like to lean upon [1] that firm arm as they walk. They do not need the help, but it is pleasant to know that help is there if needed. For that reason or some other, Maggie took Stephen's arm. They walked down the garden in a dreamy state. Stephen had had the long look into her eyes that he had wanted, but he did not feel satisfied. Maggie wondered how she came to be in the garden with Stephen. They walked in silence, each intensely conscious of the other.

'Be careful of the step,' said Stephen at last.

'Oh!' said Maggie. The spell seemed broken again by his words. 'I will go in now. Good-bye!'

She withdrew her arm and ran up the garden to the house. Back in the drawing room, she threw herself into a chair and burst into tears, thinking of Philip and wishing they were together again, so quietly, in the Red Deeps.

Stephen watched as she ran away, then he climbed into his boat. He felt angry with himself. He swore that he would never trust himself alone with Maggie again. It was madness. He was in love with Lucy; he was nearly engaged to her. He wished he had never seen Maggie Tulliver. She would make a sweet, strange, difficult, adorable wife for some man, but he would never have chosen her himself. Did she feel as he did? He hoped that she did – not.

---

1. **lean upon** : (here) support themselves on.

A C T I V I T I E S

1 Maggie enjoyed her life as a lady in high society. Why was she a social success?

2 Maggie and Stephen are both under a spell in each other's company. Which of the following sentences would you **not** associate with them in this condition. Put a cross in the column next to the sentence as in the example.

a ☒ They are embarrassed at being in each other's company.

b ☐ They feel as if they have known each other for years,

c ☐ At times they do not know what to say to each other.

d ☐ They are afraid of exposing their true feelings.

e ☐ One is easily disillusioned by even minor reactions on the part of the other.

f ☐ They understand the comic aspects of the situation.

g ☐ They are divided, on the one hand, by desire for each other's company and, on the other, by the confusion about what is happening.

h ☐ They are in control of their feelings.

i ☐ They feel more confident in each other's company.

j ☐ Their feelings for others (Maggie for Philip, Stephen for Lucy) dominate their reactions to each other.

3 The spell is broken twice. When?

4 In the next chapter Maggie meets Philip again after so long. What do you think will be the effect on Maggie of seeing Philip again?

CHAPTER 26

Philip re-enters

The next morning it was raining. Maggie and Lucy sat in the drawing room. When the doorbell rang, Lucy said, 'That will be Stephen,' and Maggie wished she could find an excuse to go upstairs. But it was not Stephen: it was Philip.

Philip had intended to act as if he and Maggie were just distant acquaintances, [1] but, when he came into the drawing room, Maggie rushed to greet him with tears in her eyes. He knew then that she must have told Lucy everything. For Maggie, seeing Philip now was a great relief, as if she had been in danger and he had come to save her. Lucy watched them with sympathy and interest. She was proud of having brought them together again, even though, looking at them side by side, she thought that her cousin Tom was not altogether wrong in feeling shocked at the idea that they could be lovers.

'It is very good of you to come to us so soon,' said Lucy.

'I should have sent a note first,' said Philip. 'But I wanted to see you, so here I am.' He spoke to Lucy, but he was looking at Maggie. Philip thought he saw a change in Maggie's look and manner.

'I am having a wonderful holiday,' said Maggie. 'Lucy won't let me do anything except enjoy myself.'

'I can see that the change is doing you good,' said Philip. 'You look very well.'

Lucy thought that this kind of conversation had gone on too long, so she pretended to have left something upstairs and went to look for it.

As soon as Lucy had left the room, Maggie took Philip's hand. 'I

---

1. **acquaintances** : (here) friends.

told my brother I wanted to see you,' she said, 'and he consented.'

'Then at least we can be friends, Maggie?' said Philip.

'Yes,' said Maggie. 'While I am here.'

'Is there no way for you to stay here forever, instead of going away from all the people who care about you?' asked Philip.

'I don't think so,' said Maggie. 'Tom says he would like to provide for me, but I want to be independent, so I must work.'

'At least until you get married,' said Philip.

'I don't think I will ever get much happiness through loving. I have always had so much pain mingled [1] with it. I wish I could make myself a world outside it, as men do.'

'You are returning to your old ideas,' said Philip bitterly. 'You think you can avoid pain by forbidding yourself any pleasure, but you can't Maggie. It's unnatural.'

'Yes. You used to tell me that in the Red Deeps,' said Maggie. 'And now I realise that you were right. You said that by denying myself pleasure I would only make myself desire it more. Now I see that I am too eager [2] in my enjoyment of music and all other pleasures. I must find work soon, or I will become accustomed to this luxurious life and feel even sadder when I have to leave it.'

Just then the doorbell rang. They heard Lucy's footsteps on the stairs and voices in the hall, then Lucy brought Stephen into the drawing room.

'Hello, Philip!' said Stephen, striding [3] over to Philip and shaking his hand. 'I'm so glad that you are back!' Then, turning to Maggie with formal politeness, he said, 'Good morning, Miss Tulliver. I hope you are well?'

'Quite well, thank you,' said Maggie, without looking at him. Philip watched them closely. He found something strange in their

---

1. **mingled** : mixed.
2. **eager** : interested.
3. **striding** : walking determinedly with long steps.

stiff formality. Lucy, however, was used to the changes in their manners towards each other. She thought that it was simply the result of an antipathy between them, which occasionally rose to the surface. Maggie was not the kind of woman Stephen admired, and Stephen was too conceited for Maggie's taste.

'This rain is making us all a little sad,' said Lucy. 'Let's have some music to cheer us up. Will you play the piano, Philip, and sing this duet with Stephen?'

'Certainly!' said Philip, and he really did want to play. He was feeling so many strong emotions at the moment – love, jealousy, resignation, suspicion – that he needed the relief of music. 'Playing the piano and painting are the two things I enjoy most.'

'And you are good at both,' said Stephen. 'Now I can't do anything with my hands. My talents are more of the administrative sort. Don't you think so, Miss Tulliver?'

Even though he had greeted Maggie with formal politeness, he had felt hurt when she responded in the same tone. Now he needed to make friends again, in their usual playful way, and he wanted her to look at him.

'You certainly like to manage everything,' replied Maggie with a glance and a smile. Philip hoped that she really found that quality in Stephen unpleasant, but somehow he doubted it.

Maggie tried to continue her sewing while they sang, but she could not. The song aroused emotions in her that made her both weak and strong: strong for all enjoyment, and weak to resist it. She put down her sewing and watched them, bending forward as the music washed over her in waves. [1] Philip, glancing up from the sheet music, thought that he had never seen her look so moved.

When the duet was over, Philip played an aria from the *Sonnambula*: 'Ah! perché non posso odiarti', in which the tenor tells

---

1. **washed over her in waves** : affected her greatly.

the heroine that he will always love her, even if she abandons him. As Maggie listened, she recognised the song: Philip had sung it to her in the Red Deeps. There seemed to be some reproach in the words. Did Philip intend that? She wished that she had told him more clearly that the only reason they could never be lovers again was because of their families.

'You tenors are so weak,' said Stephen, when Philip had finished the song. 'You are always telling the ladies that you will love them no matter how badly they treat you. I'll sing this one for contrast.' And he sang, with great energy and irony, the song that begins,

'Shall I, wasting in despair,

Die because a woman's fair?'

Maggie forced herself to return to her sewing. She did not want to listen to the song or look at the singer. Perhaps she would have relented had she known how much Stephen wished that she would look at him, how grateful he would have been for a smile.

Next, Lucy and Philip sang a duet from *The Tempest*. Stephen sat down to listen, but he kept looking at Maggie with furtive glances. When she rose from her seat and crossed the room to get a footstool, Stephen leapt up to help her. Then he placed the footstool by Maggie's chair, looking humble and anxious. These things had their effect on Maggie. 'Can I get you anything else?' asked Stephen, bending over her chair.

Maggie looked up at him and said, 'No, thank you.' They looked into each other's eyes with a feeling that was delicious to both, as it had been the evening before.

Getting the footstool for Maggie was an ordinary act of politeness. Lucy, who was singing, had hardly noticed it. But, for Philip, Stephen's sudden eagerness and the change in Maggie's face were too strong a contrast to their former stiff politeness. For him, these signs were full of painful meaning.

When it was time to leave, Lucy took Philip aside and said to him,

'Come and see me tomorrow morning. Maggie will be away at aunt Glegg's house, and I have something to tell you.'

'Very well. I'll come at ten o'clock,' said Philip. For a moment he forgot his anxieties about Maggie and wondered what Lucy could possibly want to say to him.

A   C   T   I   V   I   T   I   E   S

1 Maggie refers again to one of the two 'voices' that have always been in her. Which voice is it?

2 Whilst Lucy is unaware of what is happening to Maggie and Stephen, Philip understands 'the signs (that) were full of painful meaning'. What are the three signs which Philip understands and Lucy does not?

3 What do you think Lucy intends to tell Philip? Choose either **a**, **b** or **c**. As always, discuss your choice with a partner and then check if you were right.

a Lucy tells him she is going to marry Stephen.

b Lucy tells him that if he would like to marry Maggie they could get married at the same time.

c Lucy tells him her father is prepared to buy Dorlcote Mill.

CHAPTER 27

Wakem in a new light

A few days later, Mr Wakem came up to Philip's painting room. Philip had asked him to come and look at his work. 'Well! This is a nice place for you, isn't it, Phil?' asked Mr Wakem, looking around. 'There's good light and plenty of space for your painting things.' He had provided the room for Philip, and he liked to remind himself and his son that he had been a good father.

Mr Wakem put his glasses on and looked at the paintings and drawings that lined [1] the walls. 'This is very fine work!' he said. 'You're as good as that London artist – what's his name? I believe he makes a fortune selling his paintings.'

Philip smiled and shook his head. Mr Wakem walked slowly round the room, looking carefully at each painting, then stopped and said in surprise, 'What are these? Portraits? I thought you just did landscapes, Phil.'

'I do usually,' said Philip, rather nervously. 'Those are two portraits of the same person at different ages.'

'And who is she?' asked Mr Wakem sharply.

'Miss Tulliver. The small one is of her when she was a child, when we first knew each other at Stelling's school. The large one was done two years ago.'

Wakem took off his glasses and looked at his son rather fiercely. 'Do you mean to say that you spent time with her as recently as that?'

'Yes. I used to meet her in the woods – that place they call the Red Deeps – near Dorlcote Mill. I love her dearly. I shall never love any

---

1. **lined** : (here) were hung on.

other woman. I have loved her ever since we were children.'

'Is that so? And have you been writing to her all these years?'

'No. I never told her I loved her until just before we parted. She promised her brother that she would not see me again or write to me. I am not sure that she loves me, but, if she does, I would like to marry her.'

'What?' cried Mr Wakem, going pale. 'Is this the way you treat your father? Haven't I been a good father to you?'

'Yes, you have,' said Philip. 'And I always thought you wished me to be happy. Marrying Miss Tulliver would make me happy.'

'Her father was an ignorant brute!' said Mr Wakem. 'And her brother is insolent. He'll break every bone in your body if you are not careful. Of course, you are twenty-six years old. You are independent of me. You can marry her tomorrow if you wish. But, if you do, I will never speak to you again!'

'I couldn't marry Miss Tulliver tomorrow, Father, even if she agreed to it. I have very little money. I can't ask her to accept poverty as well as deformity.'

These last words affected Mr Wakem strongly. 'Well, this girl must be fond of you, Phil,' he said at last, 'or she would not have agreed to meet you in secret.'

'She liked me when we were children, at Stelling's, but she didn't think of me as a lover when we started meeting in the Red Deeps.'

'But what did she say when you told her you loved her?'

'She said she loved me too.'

'Well, then! What more do you want?'

'She was very young then,' said Philip. 'Perhaps she didn't really understand her own feelings. I think our long separation and the obstacles to our marriage may have made a difference. She is back in St Ogg's now. I have seen her at Mr Deane's house, but I haven't spoken to her of love again.'

'Why not?' asked Mr Wakem.

'Because of those obstacles to our marriage, Father.'

'Then why have you spoken to me about it today?'

'Well, yesterday I had a talk in private with Miss Lucy Deane. She says that her father can persuade Guest and Company to buy Dorlcote Mill from you, if you are willing. It seems that Guest and Company are very pleased with Tom Tulliver's work. They offered him a partnership, but he asked them to buy the mill instead.'

Mr Wakem frowned and walked up and down the room. Finally he said, 'I could sell the mill, I suppose, if you think that might make it easier for you. My love for your mother was the best thing in my life. I'd be sorry if you never had that kind of comfort, Phil. Come,' he said, extending his hand to his son. 'I don't want to quarrel with you. I've always done my best for you, and I'll do my best now.'

Philip smiled and shook his father's hand with relief.

A   C   T   I   V   I   T   I   E   S

1   In this chapter Wakem behaves as we would expect. He also behaves 'in a new light', in a way that possibly surprises us. Find examples of both.

Wakem as expected	Wakem in a new light
• •	• • • •

2   Which of the two lights prevail? Why do you think?

CHAPTER 28

A dance at Park House

The following Saturday evening there was a dance at Park House. As they were getting dressed for the party, Lucy told Maggie the good news. 'Guest and Company have made Mr Wakem an offer for the mill, and he has accepted it! Isn't that wonderful? You see, dear Maggie, all the obstacles to your marriage with Philip shall be removed one by one! I have been so clever! I spoke to my father about the mill, and he spoke to the Company. Then I spoke to Philip, and he spoke to his father. And now it is all done!'

'Ah!' said Maggie, with tears in her eyes. 'Then my father's last wish has come true, and Tom will have the mill again.'

'Yes, he is moving there tomorrow. And you and Philip can be married now.'

'Lucy, I too have some news,' said Maggie. 'I wrote to our old teacher Miss Firniss and asked if I could teach at her school. I received a letter from her today. She says that there is work for me, so I will be leaving on Monday.'

'Maggie!' cried Lucy. 'Why didn't you tell me before? And Philip? I thought everything was going to be so happy. Oh, Maggie, why did you do it? Write to her and tell her that you cannot come. There is nothing now to keep you and Philip apart.'

'Yes there is,' said Maggie. 'There are Tom's feelings. He said that if I married Philip he would never speak to me again, and I know he will not change.'

'Let me talk to him, Maggie,' said Lucy eagerly. 'Tom always listens to what I say.'

'But I must go,' cried Maggie, in a distressed voice. 'Don't make me stay, dear Lucy!'

As Maggie, Lucy, and Mr Deane entered the great ballroom at Park House, they remarked on how lovely it looked, brilliant with lights, flowers and music. At first Maggie refused to dance, but after a while the music was too strong a temptation, and she danced with pleasure. Stephen had decided not to ask Maggie to dance. He danced with Lucy and with some of the other young ladies, but all the time he was thinking of Maggie – of Maggie and Philip.

Some of Lucy's remarks had suggested that she thought of Maggie and Philip as lovers. Stephen began watching Philip closely, and he saw that Philip often looked at Maggie with longing in his eyes. Philip was Stephen's closest friend. Here, he told himself, was another reason to resist the attraction that was threatening to overpower him. Yet the idea of Philip as Maggie's lover was disgusting to him and made him feel even more strongly the desire to run to Maggie and claim [1] her for himself.

While dancing with Lucy, Stephen imagined himself dancing with Maggie. The thought of having her hand in his for so long was like the thought of cool water to a thirsty man. When the dance was over, Stephen saw Maggie sitting alone at the far end of the room. He made his way towards her, around the couples forming for the waltz. When Maggie became aware that he was coming to her, she felt warm and happy. Stephen bent over her with a look of tenderness. 'It is so hot in here,' he said. 'Would you like to see the conservatory?' [2]

Maggie had resolved never to be alone with him again. But now that she was leaving St Ogg's, what harm could come of enjoying herself for this one last evening? She took his arm and they walked out through the empty sitting room and into the conservatory. 'How strange the flowers look with lights among them,' said Maggie. 'They seem like flowers in a fairy story.'

Stephen said nothing and they walked on, each intensely aware of

1. **claim** : (here) take.
2. **conservatory** : room with glass walls and roof built on the side of a house.

the other's presence close by. The fact that they must soon part made these moments together painfully sweet.

They paused by a rose bush. 'Ah! How lovely the roses are!' said Maggie. 'I would like to pick one and breathe in all its scent,' and she reached upwards to pick a rose.

Who has not felt the beauty of a woman's arm? Maggie's arm was fine and shapely, like the arm of a sculpted goddess from the Parthenon, but warm and alive. Stephen leapt forward impulsively and kissed Maggie's arm. But Maggie snatched [1] her arm away from him and glared at him, trembling with anger and humiliation.

'How dare you? What right have I given you to insult me!' she cried. She ran away from him, back to the empty sitting room, and threw herself on the sofa. This was her punishment for the sin of allowing herself a moment's happiness that was treachery [2] to Lucy, to Philip – to her own better soul. Stephen came up to her, looking humble and miserable. 'Please leave me alone,' she said. He wanted to beg her forgiveness, but he felt he must obey her. When he returned to the ballroom, the waltz was not yet over.

Maggie went back to the ballroom after a few minutes. She did not dance again that evening, but she talked to people and watched the dancing, and slowly her composure returned. She felt finally free from the fascination that had been tempting her for the past weeks. Now, she felt, she could leave without regret. She could do her duty willingly. And, as she rode home in the carriage holding Lucy's hand, she felt grateful that she had been saved from hurting her gentle unsuspecting cousin.

The next morning Philip came to visit. Maggie sat alone with him in the garden. 'I have found new work, Philip,' she said gently. 'I am leaving tomorrow for Miss Firniss's school.'

'Why, Maggie?' asked Philip in distress. 'You know the mill will

---

1. **snatched** : quickly took.
2. **treachery** : betrayal, very hurtful.

soon be your brother's home again. I told my father all about our meetings in the Red Deeps. He was angry at first, but he is not angry anymore, and he wants to meet you, Maggie.'

'I'm sorry, Philip,' said Maggie. 'I can't. Tom would never forgive me. I desire no future that will break the ties of the past, and the tie

to my brother is one of the strongest. I can't do anything willingly that will divide me from him.'

'Is that the only reason?' asked Philip, looking at her closely.

'Yes,' said Maggie, and she believed it.

A C T I V I T I E S

1 Lucy is convinced that Maggie and Philip are lovers. She wants to help them and she has tried to remove the obstacles to their marriage 'one by one'. What has she done so far?

a   ....

b   ....

c   (Maggie tells her about Tom's opposition to the marriage. Lucy will resolve this problem, too): ....
....

2 However, there is one obstacle she doesn't know about which she cannot overcome. What is it?

3 Maggie is again divided by her sense of self-sacrifice and loyalty to others, and her attraction to Stephen. In chapter 28, the former dominates and both Stephen and Philip are affected as a result. How?

4 Do you think Maggie is now fully convinced that she can leave St Ogg's to go to Miss Firniss' school 'without regret'?

CHAPTER 29

Borne along [1] by the tide [2]

That afternoon, Lucy and Mr Deane went to tea at Mr and Mrs Glegg's. Maggie stayed home. She had told them that she needed time to pack her things, but in fact she simply wanted to be alone in peace for a while. She was walking in the garden, listening to the birds singing and enjoying the scent of the roses, when suddenly she heard footsteps coming from the river. She looked up and saw Stephen hurrying towards her with an anxious expression on his face.

'Oh, why did you come?' asked Maggie, her heart beating fast.

'Lucy told me last night that you are leaving. I could not let you go in that way, angry with me as you were. Are you still angry with me?' he looked at her with humble anxious eyes.

'No. But you must leave. Lucy and her father are at my aunt Glegg's. I am alone. Please leave.'

'Of course, you are angry with me again for coming here,' said Stephen bitterly. 'You don't care what I suffer. All you care about is your own dignity.'

Maggie started, as if she had received a slight electric shock.

'You don't care that I am going mad with love for you, that I am trying to resist the strongest passion a man can feel, because I don't want to hurt other people. No! You think I am a brute! You think I mean to insult you! But, if I were free, I would ask you to marry me, to share my fortune and my life. I know I behaved badly last night. I hate myself for having done it. But you should forgive me, because I love you with my whole soul.'

'You must not say these things. I must not hear them,' said

---

1. **Borne along** : transported.   2. **tide** : currents caused by high water.

Maggie, looking down. 'I'm sorry if I have caused you pain, but it's no use talking about it.'

Stephen looked at her closely. 'Maggie, it is of use,' he said at last. 'If I thought you loved me, I would do anything so that we could be together forever. We could break the mistaken ties [1] we have made and marry each other.'

'I would rather die than fall into that temptation,' said Maggie.

Stephen was silent for a long time. 'Well, Maggie,' he said at last. 'Come with me on the river in the boat for one more ride before we part.' His voice was tremulous, and Maggie felt a sharp pain herself because of the pain she was causing him.

'We shouldn't,' she said in a weak voice. 'Lucy would be hurt if she knew.'

'We won't be long,' said Stephen. 'You will be back before they get home.'

And they went. Stephen led Maggie down the garden, between the rose bushes. He helped her into the boat, and got in himself. They glided [2] rapidly along the river. Stephen watched Maggie as he rowed, but she was looking at the banks of the Floss, the houses and trees slipping by. Then she sank into a dreamy state and did not notice the villages they were passing. She only felt the sun's warmth and heard the birds singing and the rhythmic sound of the dipping [3] oars. Suddenly she was aware that Stephen had stopped rowing. The boat was moving along by itself on the tide. She sat up and looked anxiously at the banks of the river. 'Where are we?' she asked. 'Have we passed Luckreth?'

'Yes,' said Stephen in a dreamy absent tone. 'Yes – a long way.'

'But we had to turn back at Luckreth!' cried Maggie. 'We shall be late, and Lucy – Oh God, help me!'

'Maggie,' said Stephen. 'Let's never go home again, until we are married.'

---

1. **ties** : connections.
2. **glided** : floated.
3. **dipping** : going into the water.

Maggie sat silent, hardly breathing.

'The tide was swifter [1] than I thought,' said Stephen, in a low, earnest voice. 'And I was looking at you. I didn't notice how far we had come. The tide bore us along without our knowing it. It will carry us on to Mudport. We can land there and get a carriage to Scotland, where we can be married, then no one will ever be able to separate us again.'

Maggie wanted to believe what he was saying – that the tide was doing it all, and that she could glide along with the swift silent stream and not struggle anymore. But still the voices of the past were calling to her. She could not hurt Lucy and Philip. 'No! You must have known we had gone too far! Let me go!' she cried.

'All right,' said Stephen. 'We will go back, and I will tell Lucy that I was mad, and that you hate me.' He spoke in a trembling voice, full of repressed rage.

Maggie was paralysed. How could she go back and blame everything on Stephen when she herself had been so weak? And Lucy would know. Lucy would be hurt. Stephen was right: it was too late now to save Lucy from pain. The boat was still drifting [2] down the river. 'Of course I couldn't do that,' she said.

When we yield [3] to temptation, we are in a dreamy state. Our thoughts are half asleep. Maggie did not say or do anything decisive, but that was itself a kind of consent. The boat continued drifting on the swift tide. At last, Stephen took up the oars again. He looked at Maggie, and she looked back at him, dreamy and passive. Stephen started to row the boat. He rowed quickly, because they had to get to Mudport before the sun set.

It was a long way to Mudport, and as they rowed downstream the sun disappeared behind clouds and the air became chilly. Stephen's arms ached from the rowing, but he rowed on quickly, watching

1. **swifter** : quicker.
2. **drifting** : floating.   3. **yield** : agree.

Maggie's face. Maggie was cold and trembling by the time they arrived. Stephen landed the boat and helped Maggie out, then he led her to a hotel on the river bank.

'This lady – my wife – needs a room,' said Stephen to the hotel manager. 'We went too far in our rowing boat, and now she is chilled and tired.'

The manager led them to a comfortable room, but at the door Stephen said, 'I will wait for you downstairs. Sleep, dear Maggie. We're safe now.'

Maggie closed the door and lay down on the large soft bed. Almost immediately, she fell into a deep sleep. She slept for a long time and woke in the early hours of the morning. But just before waking she had a dream. In the dream she was on the river in the boat with Stephen. It was evening and darkness was gathering. Across the water, she saw something glowing, like the light of the moon. She watched as it got closer until finally she saw that it was the Virgin sitting in St Ogg's boat. As it got nearer, she saw that the Virgin was Lucy and the boatman was Philip – no, not Philip, but Tom. He rowed past without looking at her. She stood up in the boat and reached her arms out to him, but her movement caused the boat to overturn, and they began to sink.

She woke up with a start. At first she did not understand where she was, but then it all came back to her: the terrible thing that she and Stephen had done, the sorrow she had caused the people she had loved since childhood. Maggie leapt up from the bed and went downstairs to find Stephen. He was in the drawing room, pacing [1] up and down. He looked tired and worn. As soon as he saw her face, he knew what she was going to say.

'Stephen, we must go home,' said Maggie, in a firm, earnest voice. 'We must go back immediately.'

---

1. **pacing** : walking nervously.

1 There are several idioms in English using the noun 'tide'. To find them, look in your English learner's dictionary. One is 'borne by the tide of events'. What does it mean in general and, in particular, in chapter 29?

2 These events make up Maggie and Stephen's journey down the river. Put them into the correct order.

a ☐ Maggie dreams of Lucy as the Virgin.

b ☐ Stephen starts rowing again to Mudport.

c ☐ Stephen helps Maggie into the boat.

d ☐ Maggie realises that it is too late to go back to St Ogg's.

e ☐ They stay at a hotel in Mudport.

f ☐ Stephen asks Maggie to go for one more ride on the river.

g ☐ Stephen tells Maggie that they can continue to Mudport in order to go to Scotland to get married.

h ☐ She wakes up and insists on going back to St Ogg's.

i ☐ Stephen stopped rowing and the boat moved down the river passed Luckreth.

j ☐ Maggie and Stephen arrive at Mudport.

3 Maggie's voice of self-sacrifice is seriously challenged in chapter 29. In what state is she (and Stephen) when she follows the other 'voice'? What recurring vocabulary do you notice? Compare it to a similar 'state' in chapter 25 'Under a spell'.

4 Do you remember the legend of St Ogg's (see chapter 1)? Interpret Maggie's dream. Compare your interpretation with a partner.

5 How do you think Tom will greet his sister on her return to St Ogg's?

PART 4

1 Relatives

a Think of your immediate family (father, mother, brothers, sisters) and your extended family (aunts, uncles). Choose a relative to describe. Consider some of the following ideas:
- A relative you particularly admire.
- Somebody unusual in your family, (eccentric, special talent, notable achievement).
- Someone you are particularly close to.
- A relative with whom you have a difficult or conflicting relationship.
- Someone in your family who you would like to know better.

b You are going to describe the relative you have chosen to a partner. Think of the vocabulary you will need to describe:
Personality; physical appearance; reasons why you have chosen this person.

c Your partner will ask you questions.

d When you listen to your partner's description ask questions to find out more information.

e Write your description in around 200 words.

2 Part 4 was longer in comparison to parts 1, 2 and 3. Try and complete the main events from 'Temptation' by starting with the most recent event and then go backwards! The most recent event in chapter 29 and the first event in part 4 from chapter 21 have been done for you. Go backwards in the story trying to remember the events until you reach event no. 12. Work with a partner. Only look at the story when you have finished (or if you are stuck!). Add the chapter number.

Event no.	Event	Chapter
1	Maggie returns to St Ogg's from Mudport	29
2		

Event no.	Event	Chapter
3		
4		
5		
6		
7		
8		
9		
10		
11		
12	Lucy tells Stephen that her cousin Maggie is coming to stay with her	21

3 Join some of the events from part 4 into a short text by starting with the most recent event and then going backwards. Use phrases such as *By the time...; this happened because previously...; just before this Maggie/Stephen/Philip had...* Be careful of the combination of narrative tenses (past simple and past perfect).

4 What is your opinion of Stephen, and of Maggie's decision to be 'borne by the tide'? Discuss your ideas in a small group.

PART 5
THE FINAL RESCUE

CHAPTER ◆ 30

The return to the mill

T om was back at the mill. He had made his family name
respectable once more. Once again they were the Tullivers
of Dorlcote Mill. But there was no look of triumph on
Tom's face as he stood by the mill wheel, watching the rush of the
water. His mouth wore a bitter expression. No news had been heard of
his sister since she had run off with Mr Stephen Guest. Someone from
St Ogg's had seen them entering a hotel in Mudport the previous
evening. Would the next news be that they were married? Probably
not. Tom expected the worst to happen: not death but disgrace.

The booming of the water was so loud that at first he did not hear
her calling his name, but then he looked round and saw Maggie
standing by the gate. She looked tired and lonely. It is just as I
thought, he said to himself in disgust.

'Tom,' said Maggie in a faint voice. 'I have come back to you – I
have come home. I will tell you everything.'

'You will find no home with me,' replied Tom angrily. 'You have
disgraced us all. You have hurt everyone closest to you. You have
been wicked and deceitful. 1 I never want to see you again. You don't
belong to me.'

---

1. **deceitful** : dishonest.

◆ *151* ◆

Mrs Tulliver appeared at the door. She stood there, paralysed by the double shock of seeing Maggie and hearing Tom's words.

'Tom,' said Maggie, with more courage. 'I am not as guilty as you think. I never meant to give way to my feelings. I struggled against them. I was carried too far in the boat yesterday. I came back as soon as I could.'

'I don't believe you!' said Tom. 'You have been carrying on a secret relationship with Stephen Guest, just as you did before with someone else. You have been using Philip Wakem to deceive Lucy. Go and see what you have done! She's ill!'

'I'm sorry, Tom,' cried Maggie. 'I know I have done wrong, and I repent. Keep me from doing wrong again.'

'Nothing will keep you from doing wrong!' cried Tom. 'You say you struggled with your feelings. I have struggled with my feelings too, and I conquered them. I have had a harder life than you, but I found comfort in doing my duty. I will provide for you, if you want, but you shall not live in this house. The sight of you is hateful to me.'

Maggie turned away, with despair in her heart, but just then she heard her mother's voice crying out, 'My child! I'll go with you! You still have a mother!'

Mrs Tulliver ran up to Maggie and threw her arms around her, then they went off together, hand in hand.

'Where shall I go, Mother?' asked Maggie, sadly.

'I don't know,' said Mrs Tulliver. 'We could go to your aunt Glegg's house, but I'm a bit afraid of what she'll say.'

'No. Let's go to Bob Jakin's house. He has plenty of room in the round house.'

When they got to the old house by the river, Bob himself opened the door. He asked no questions, but showed Maggie to a pleasant room on the ground floor. He told his mother and his wife to make everything comfortable for her.

That evening, when they were alone in their room, Maggie tried to explain what had happened to her mother. 'When I told him we had to go home, he was very angry. We argued about it for hours. He said that the damage was already done. We had already hurt Lucy and Philip, and to go home now would just hurt ourselves without doing any good to them. But I had to come home! And so finally I left him, and made my way home alone. I hope I did the right thing,' said poor Maggie. 'I'm so worried about Lucy.'

'I just saw your uncle Deane,' said Mrs Tulliver, 'and he told me that he received a letter from Mudport – from Mr Stephen Guest – delivered by horseman this morning. The letter says that he is going abroad. He begs Lucy's forgiveness and explains that neither he nor you ever wanted to hurt her. He says that you are not at all to blame for what happened. Your uncle Deane says he read the letter to Lucy, and she seems calmer now.'

'Oh, thank God!' said Maggie. 'And Philip Wakem? Have you heard anything of him?'

'Well, no,' said Mrs Tulliver, 'but they say that his father is very upset. You see, he told some people in St Ogg's that he was allowing his son to court you. Then, when this news came, he looked a bit of a fool, you see. It must have been very humiliating for him. He's a proud man.'

A   C   T   I   V   I   T   I   E   S

1   Tom's reaction to Maggie's return is predictable. However, he unjustly accuses her of having done something. What is it?

2   What extra information do we learn about Maggie's journey down the river with Stephen?

3   People suffered as a result of Maggie's actions. How?

Tom:
Lucy:
Stephen:
Wakem:

CHAPTER 31

The last conflict

Mrs Tulliver stayed with Maggie at Bob Jakin's house for the first two days, but then Maggie told her to go back to the mill and take care of Tom. She wanted to be alone with her sorrow.

Maggie lived very quietly at Bob's house for the rest of the summer. When Lucy was a little better, she asked Maggie to come and see her. Lucy told Maggie that she forgave her, and the two cousins cried in each other's arms. A few days later, Maggie received a noble, loving letter from Philip. He said he understood that she had never meant to hurt him. He said he would always be there if she needed him. He mentioned bad headaches and said he never left his father's house these days.

Autumn came, and with it the rains. Bob shook his head and said he had never seen such rains, but he remembered his grandfather telling him that it had rained for days and days before the last great flood.

The hours were very long and dreary for Maggie. She sat in her room, looking out of the window and watching the raindrops pelting [1] the surface of river. Even when it was not raining, Maggie never went into town. She knew that she was the subject of gossip there, and she thought that if they did not see her, people would forget her and all her mistakes. Soon she would be going away, for Miss Firniss had written to say that she could come and teach at the school after Christmas. It made Maggie very sad to think about starting a new life, going to a new place and seeing new faces. She was so tired!

One day in September, she received a letter. It was from Stephen.

---

1. **pelting** : hitting.

He was at Mudport, but he had not yet told his family that he was back in England. From beginning to end, the letter was a passionate cry of reproach. Why had she sacrificed his hopes and hers? What was the point in choosing to suffer, when their suffering could not save Lucy and Philip from suffering? Did she not realise how much he – Stephen – was suffering? He could not live without her. 'Maggie! Write me one word – say, "Come!" – and I will be there with you. Have you forgotten what it was like to be together?'

Maggie felt that her real temptation had only just begun. Again she struggled with her own desires. She thought of her meeting with Lucy and of Philip's letter. They had both been so loving and forgiving. Surely to answer Stephen's plea [1] would cause them more pain. But Stephen himself sounded so miserable! And she was miserable too! All she had to do was write one word – 'Come!' – and their misery would be over, this dreary lonely life would be at an end.

All day she struggled against her longing to send him that one word. Night came, and the rain pelted the window pane, [2] and still Maggie sat up reading and re-reading Stephen's letter. She tried to sleep but could not, though it was past four o'clock. Finally, she fell to her knees and began to pray, 'Oh God, must I struggle and fall and repent again? Will all my life be like this? I am so young and strong – how will I bear all those years of pain?'

At that moment, Maggie felt a sudden coldness around her knees and feet. Looking down, she saw that the floor was covered in water. Maggie jumped up and ran to Bob's bedroom, crying, 'Bob! Wake up! The flood has come! Get up! We must make sure that the boats are safe.'

Bob leapt up. The water was rising fast. Maggie and Bob waded [3] through the water to the back door. Outside, by the light of the moon,

---

1. **plea** : supplication.
2. **pane** : piece of glass.
3. **waded** : walked.

they saw the two row-boats bobbing [1] on the surface of the water, not far away. 'They're safe!' cried Bob. 'I must get my mother and my wife into a boat!' Then he was suddenly struck by the fact that Maggie had noticed the flood, had woken him, and had taken the lead in activity. It seemed to Bob that she was one of those who would protect, not one who would need protection.

'I'll take the other boat!' said Maggie. 'I must go to the mill to help my brother and my mother!'

Quickly Maggie got into the boat and took the oars. She started to row the boat as Stephen had taught her, and suddenly all her troubles and struggles were gone. She felt nothing. The moon set behind the hill, and she was alone in the dark with God.

She imagined Tom asleep in the mill as the water rose around him. 'Oh God!' she cried. 'Where am I? Which way is home?'

She was floating in smooth water now, over the flooded fields. Gradually, the sky began to get paler, and she recognised the black forms of trees and buildings. She rowed as fast as she could in the direction of the mill. On she rowed in her wet clothes, her black hair streaming in the wind. On she rowed towards her brother, feeling a strong resurgence of love for him, hoping that they could be reconciled by this great disaster. The water was moving very fast, and the broken limbs [2] of trees were sailing along with the tide. For the first time, Maggie realised that she was in danger.

When she got to the mill, she saw that the water had reached the first storey. [3] She called out in a loud, piercing [4] voice, 'Tom! Where are you?'

Tom opened a window at the level of the boat. 'Maggie! Are you alone?'

---

1. **bobbing** : moving up and down.
2. **limbs** : (here) parts, pieces.
3. **storey** : floor.
4. **piercing** : high, penetrating.

'Yes. God has taken care of me, to bring me to you. Go and get Mother quickly.'

Tom climbed out of the window and into the boat. 'Mother is staying at my aunt Deane's house,' he said. 'Give me the oars, Maggie.'

The sun was just beginning to rise as Tom rowed away from the mill. He sat opposite Maggie and looked at her in awe. 1 The full meaning of what had just happened rushed upon his mind. He had always thought that he saw things clearly, but he had been wrong about Maggie: she was a brave, noble woman. Maggie's eyes were full of intense life, though her face was weary. It seemed a miracle to him that she – a woman alone – could have rowed the boat all the way to the mill in darkness to save him. At last tears came into his eyes, and he said the only thing he could find to say, his old childish name for her: 'Magsie!'

Maggie sobbed with happiness and pain. 'Let's go and see if Mother and Lucy are safe, Tom. Then we can go and help others.'

Just then a great piece of floating wood appeared in the water in front of them. Tom looked up and saw Death rushing towards them. He let go of the oars and clasped 2 her in his arms. 'It is coming, Maggie!' he cried.

The next moment the boat was no longer to be seen on the water. Brother and sister had gone down in an embrace never to be parted – remembering the days when they had clasped their little hands in love and roamed 3 the fields together.

1. **awe** [ɔː] : admiration.
2. **clasped** : held tightly.
3. **roamed** : walked.

1   'Lucy, Philip and Stephen react to the events as we would expect.' How
    do they react and why is their reaction 'as we would expect'?

2   Maggie's inner struggle continues. What arguments does she consider
    in favour of both 'voices'?

Self-sacrifice	Desire for love and happiness
•	•
•	•
	•

3   Why does Tom say 'Magsie'?

Conclusion

A fter the flood, two bodies were buried together in Dorlcote churchyard. Two men visited the tomb very often, both feeling that their greatest joy and their greatest sorrow were buried there. One of them visited the tomb again with a sweet face beside him, but that was years later. The other was always solitary, remembering his times in the Red Deeps. The tomb bore [1] the names of Tom and Maggie Tulliver, and below their names was written, 'In their death they were not divided.' [2]

---

1. **bore** : (here) carried.
2. **In ...divided** : this is a quotation from the Bible, from David's lament for Jonathan (2 Samuel 1:23).

A   C   T   I   V   I   T   I   E   S

1 Who do you think were the two men who visited the tomb?

2 What is the significance of the inscription 'In their death they were not divided'?

PART 5

1 Stephen Guest has been regarded by many critics as representing a weak point in the novel. Walter Allen wrote that he is 'simply not adequate to a young woman of Maggie's fineness of sensibility and discrimination' and their relationship 'spoils her (Eliot's) novel'.

Do you agree? Discuss your ideas in a group and make a note of your ideas.

2 Critics have also regarded the ending as unsatisfactory. Allen, again, was particularly critical:

'If you have a river in a novel, a flood is always tempting; but by yielding to the temptation, George Eliot, instead of allowing Maggie to resolve the moral dilemma in which she found herself, and live by its consequences, took the easy way and substituted for a genuine resolution a cliché-ending from the stock of Victorian fiction.'

Can you propose an alternative ending? In groups discuss your ideas and what you would change. Limit your changes to part 5. Write a brief summary of your ending and make copies for the other groups in your class. When you have read the ideas of the other groups, decide on one for the whole class. Write a final class version. Use the same style you used for the summaries of parts 1 to 3.